PERGAMON SERIES OF MONOGRAPHS ON
FURNITURE AND TIMBER
GENERAL EDITOR: JACK KAPE

VOLUME 5

TIMBER PESTS AND DISEASES

PERGAMON SERIES OF MONOGRAPHS ON
FURNITURE AND TIMBER

Head of walking-stick infected with Furniture Beetle

Timber Pests
and Diseases

W. P. K. FINDLAY, D. SC., F.I.W. SC.

PERGAMON PRESS

OXFORD · LONDON · EDINBURGH · NEW YORK
TORONTO · SYDNEY · PARIS · BRAUNSCHWEIG

Pergamon Press Ltd., Headington Hill Hall, Oxford
4 & 5 Fitzroy Square, London W. 1
Pergamon Press (Scotland) Ltd., 2 & 3 Teviot Place, Edinburgh 1
Pergamon Press Inc., 44-01 21st Street, Long Island City, New York 11101
Pergamon of Canada, Ltd., 6 Adelaide Street East, Toronto, Ontario
Pergamon Press (Aust.) Pty. Ltd., 20-22 Margaret Street, Sydney, N.S.W.
Pergamon Press S.A.R.L., 24 rue des Ecoles, Paris 5ᵉ
Vieweg & Sohn GmbH, Burgplatz 1, Braunschweig.

First edition 1967

Library of Congress Catalog Card No. 65-17951

Printed in Italy - SAIPEM Cassino-Rome

2334/67

Contents

List of Illustrations

Preface

THIS book is based on an earlier work, entitled *Dry Rot and Other Timber Troubles*, which is now out of print.

The opportunity has been taken to revise the text throughout, bringing it up to date and including the results of recent research work. A new chapter on Termites has been included. Detailed reference to wood preservatives has been omitted as modern works dealing with this subject have recently been published in this country.

For permission to reproduce the undermentioned photographs grateful thanks are due to the following:

The Director of the Forest Products Research Laboratory for all the photographs noted as C.C.R., (Crown Copyright Reserved).

Mr. S. A. Richardson Frontispiece and Fig. 12.

Dr. L. Harmsen Fig. 13.

Danish Statens Skadedslaboratorium Fig. 13b.

Messrs. Cuprinol Ltd. Figs. 18 and 26.

Mr. A. H. Thompson Fig. 22.

Mr. S. H. Loweth Figs. 44 and 45.

Mr. W. R. Day Fig. 43.

Messrs. Farebrother, Ellis & Co. Fig. 42.

Mr. W. V. Harris Figs. 23, 24 and 25.

Commonwealth Experimental Building Station Fig. 27.

Mr. H. A. Hyde Fig. 53.

Dr. Douglas P. Wilson Fig. 56.

The Controller of H.M. Stationery Office has kindly permitted the reproduction of certain figures that have appeared in *Forest Research Products Research Leaflets* Nos. 14, 50 and 54.

CHAPTER 1

Economic Significance of Timber Pests and Diseases

TIMBER, to primitive man, was the most useful of all the readily available materials, and from it he made his dwellings, his boats and his tools. It is still one of the most essential raw materials for his civilized descendants who have learned to use it for an ever-increasing range of purposes.

Though it is now possible to process the crude material by various methods so as to endow it with desirable properties which it may lack in its natural state, yet large amounts of wood are still used in a virtually raw condition. Much of the deterioration which occurs is due to failure to give wood the prior seasoning and treatment necessary for the particular purpose in hand.

In the days when the bulk of the timber supplies came from virgin forests which had cost nothing to plant or maintain, and when it was hewn by lowly paid labour, it was an extraordinarily cheap material. Indeed, during the pioneering days in countries such as Canada and the United States of America lumber could almost have been regarded as a by-product, obtained during the clearing of the land for agriculture. At times the settlers did not even trouble to harvest the timber, but burnt the trees as they stood, or after they had been felled. Right up to the present time methods of exploitation have remained wasteful by European standards. While timber was so cheap and readily available it is small wonder that its prema-

1

ture decay and replacement excited little interest excpet when the structure of which it formed part was of unusual value owing to the amount of labour involved in its construction, as in the case of a ship. It is interesting to note that nearly all the early books and pamphlets dealing with decay of timber refer to ships and boats.

When timber was plentiful and there was a range of species available from which to choose, the most durable kinds could be selected for those purposes, such as boat building, where durability was essential. Daniel Defoe, writing in 1724, mentions that the Sussex iron works were carried on:

"at such a prodigious expense of wood, that even in a country almost over-run with timber, they began to complain of the consuming of it for the furnaces and leaving the next age to want timber for building";

but he thought the complaint groundless, considering the counties of Kent, Sussex and Hampshire "one inexhaustible storehouse of timber". Many people in other lands have since fallen into the same error of considering their timber supply inexhaustible.

Owing to the demands for Oak from the shipbuilders, and to the destruction of the Wealden Oak forests for charcoal (used for the smelting of iron), supplies of Oak became insufficient during the eighteenth century, and softwoods from abroad began to be imported on a large scale for building the ever increasing number of houses needed for the rising population.

It is significant that we find the first references to dry rot in buildings soon after the replacement of Oak by softwoods began. In many of the more recently developed countries this stage has just been reached; and it is only within the last few years that New Zealand and Australia, having depleted their supplies of naturally durable hardwoods, have had to turn to the less durable native, or exotic species, and to study methods for rendering these resistant to decay.

Today, when the world demand for timber and other forest products has outstripped the supply, and their prices have risen steeply, there is everywhere an increasing desire to obtain the maximum service from every piece of timber used, and to avoid having to replace woodwork which has failed through premature decay.

Decay of timber should never be accepted as inevitable. If the wooden parts of any structure decay while the rest of it is still serviceable one must conclude that the woodwork was not adequately protected or preserved.

Some idea of the wastage of timber caused by premature decay may be obtained from the fact that in 1924 it was estimated that the annual loss in the United States of America from decay in wood products was in the region of 400,000,000 dollars. Even in Great Britain, where a high proportion of the timber used in vulnerable situations (i.e. in contact with the ground) receives preservative treatment, the annual wastage is still considerable. It was estimated that before 1939 the cost of making good the damage caused by dry rot in houses amounted to £1,000,000 a year. After 1945 probably ten times that sum was spent annually on repairs necessitated by dry rot in buildings. There is also a very considerable wastage from decay of timber used for other purposes. For instance, on practically every farm one can see rotting posts and gates, and in many gardens the rose pergolas lean at drunken angles, and the greenhouses and frames are in urgent need of repair. Then one has only to walk along any suburban street and notice the miles of fencing leaning at every angle from the vertical to realize how much timber would be required to replace it, and how much money would have been saved had it received proper preservative treatment in the first place.

3

In every boat yard there are always small craft under repair, and there is usually a melancholy collection of the frames of older boats that have decayed beyond repair. Even in vehicles such as motor-buses and lorries, with relatively short working lives, fungal decay of wooden parts may (particularly under tropical conditions) necessitate extensive repairs to bodywork before the chassis itself wears out.

It has not yet been found possible to give even a rough estimate of the annual loss caused by termites—the so-called White Ants—in buildings in tropical countries, but in every place where they occur it must amount to a formidable sum. A survey made in Jamaica in 1943 disclosed that approximately two thirds of all buildings on the island were infested with these insects. Inquiries, made by the West African Building Research Station, into the cost of repairing termite damage in official buildings in the four British West African territories in 1955 indicated that it amounted to about £250,000 per annum—or 10 per cent of the estimated value of the buildings. In the federation of Malaya it was estimated that in 1953 the annual cost of repairs to Government buildings, following termite attacks, was over £75,000.

Although in temperate countries insects do not cause quite such spectacular losses as the termites cause in the tropics, yet on aggregate they are responsible for widespread and extensive damage. There is evidence to show that the Common Furniture Beetle, long known as a pest in furniture, has in recent years become more prevalent in buildings, attacking flooring and structural timbers. The damage which it causes sometimes makes it necessary to replace whole floors, or to remove entire roofs. The notorious Death-Watch Beetle, with its preference for large Oak beams, has been responsible for many appeals for large sums of money with which to restore famous buildings and churches, rendered unsafe by its tunnellings. The House Longhorn Beetle, which has long been a major cause of

4

damage in the roofing timbers of buildings in Denmark and North-West Germany, has recently been found causing extensive damage to the roofs of houses in parts of Surrey, and the possibility of its spreading to other areas cannot be ignored.

Insect attack often follows fungal decay and both types of damage may be found in the same piece of wood. Conditions conducive to fungal decay often encourage attack by insects, and partially decayed wood appears to be particularly attractive to many kinds of beetle.

Since the treatment required to eradicate insects is different from that needed to arrest fungal decay it is important to be able to distinguish between the two types of attack, and find out which is the primary cause of the deterioration, and which is active when the curative measures have to be taken. Again there are occasions when the damage caused by chemical attack may simulate fungal decay. In this book emphasis has therefore been laid on the need for accurate diagnosis of the cause of deterioration before any remedial measures are taken.

B

CHAPTER 2

The Nature of Wood

WOOD is an organic material, formed during the growth of a tree by the subdivision and elongation of cells. These cells are produced by the layer of living tissue under the bark, which is known as the cambium. The cells formed by the cambium become modified and specialized to perform the various functions which the xylem, or wood, of the tree fulfils. These functions are, firstly, to provide mechanical support for the trunk and branches; secondly, to transport water for the leaves and growing tissues; and thirdly, to act as a storehouse for the reserve food materials formed by the leaves during the periods of active growth. As a tree gets larger and the diameter of the trunk increases, only the outer portion of the trunk continues to perform the last two functions, and the wood in the centre of the trunk ceases to contain living cells and contributes only to the mechanical support of the tree. This explains why many hollow old trees are still able to bear leaves and flowers and fruit.

The outer ring of wood containing the living cells is known as the *sapwood*. When these cells die changes take place which often alter the colour of the wood. This darker inner wood is called the *heartwood*. Not all kinds of tree form a definite heartwood, but even in trees such as Beech, where there is no obvious distinction between the inner and the outer zones, there are no vital activities in the inner layers of the wood. In trees in which there is a distinction in colour between the sapwood and the heartwood it will invariably be found that the timber from the heartwood shows a higher resistance to fungal decay and insect attack than from the sapwood, so this change is of particular interest to the student of timber diseases.

The nature of the changes which occur when sapwood turns into heartwood are not all fully understood, but they usually involve the production of substances such as tannins which are naturally toxic to many fungi, and which act as preservatives of the wood after the vital activities have ceased.

SOFT AND HARD WOODS

The timbers of commercial value fall into two main classes, known popularly as " softwoods " and " hardwoods ", the former being derived from coniferous trees and the latter from broad leaved. It is true that many broad-leaved trees, such as Poplar and Willow, yield quite soft timber, but the use of the terms is so well established that their meaning is well understood by timber merchants and users. We now even hear some of the lightweight woods from tropical broad-leaved trees described as " soft hardwoods ", though it would really be better to refer to them as " light hardwoods ".

On looking at the end grain of a piece of wood one notices the presence of concentric rings in which the grain is denser than it is elsewhere. In trees grown in a temperate climate each ring represents the increase in girth during a single growing season. The more open grain in a ring consists of thin-walled elements formed during the spring, and of a denser zone, formed in the summer, for thicker-walled elements. The quality of timber from trees grown in the temperate zone largely depends on the width of the annual rings, and the relative proportions of spring and summer wood in each ring. The annual rings vary in width according to the rate at which the tree is growing, and this in its turn depends on the soil, the rainfall, and the amount of light which the crown of the tree receives (i.e. how closely the trees are growing together). Softwoods are strongest when they come from trees which have grown at a moderate rate, so that there are between 8 and 20 annual rings to each inch of radial growth. The timber from conifers that have grown very rapidly tends to be coarse and weak, while that from coniferous trees grown very slowly in the far North is fine in texture, and, while admirably suited for high class joinery, is less strong than that from trees of a moderate rate of growth.

In some hardwoods, such as Ash and Oak, the best and toughest timber is found in trees that have grown quickly and have formed a high proportion of dense summer wood in each annual ring. In other hardwoods which have a uniform texture, such as Beech, the rate of growth has only a slight effect on density and strength.

Generally speaking the rate of growth of the tree has only a very slight influence on the durability of the wood, and within wide limits timber that has grown quickly is as resistant to fungal decay as is the slow grown.

There are great differences in the structure of the two classes of timber; softwoods, from conifers, having a very much simpler structure than hardwoods, from broad-leaved trees; and these differences can readily be distinguished under the microscope. If a piece of coniferous wood is disintegrated (macerated) so that the cells become separated one from another, it is seen to consist almost entirely of elongated, cigar-shaped cells, known as *tracheids*. These tracheids dovetail into each other end to end, those from the spring wood having thin walls and a wide lumen, or open space down the centre, up which the sap can pass, while those from the summer wood have much thicker walls. In the walls of the tracheids there are a number of openings, which are known as pits, and which can act like valves controlling the flow of the sap from one cell to the next.

8

Similar examination of a hardwood will reveal the presence of quite a number of different elements: firstly, portions of the vessels which in the wood fit together rather like drainpipes to give continuous tubes up which the sap can pass; secondly, tracheids similar to those found in softwoods; thirdly, thick-walled, spear-shaped fibres, pointed at both ends, and finally, brick-shaped thin-walled cells known as *parenchyma*, in which food materials such as starch are stored.

When a thin slice, or section, cut across the grain of the wood is examined under the microscope, the way in which these various elements is arranged can readily be seen. In a section of Oak the large pores, which are the ends of the vessels cut across, are confined to the spring wood portion of the ring; while in a Beech section the vessels are more or less evenly distributed throughout the width of the ring. Woods like Oak, which have the large pores only in the spring wood, are described as " ring porous ", while those with the pores generally distributed, and all approximately the same size, are known as " diffuse porous ". It is by such features that hardwoods are classified and can be recognized.

There are lines of tissue running out radially towards the bark. These are the so-called " rays ", which are ribbons of soft tissue, composed mainly of brick shaped thin-walled cells in which the reserve food materials are stored during periods of active growth, to be used later when a new crop of leaves is formed, or when the tree bears fruit and flowers. The rays also serve to some extent for the horizontal movement of the sap. The width and number of these rays is another useful diagnostic character. It is generally possible to identify almost any piece of wood by microscopic examination of its anatomical structure.

Though it is possible to learn a good deal about the mechanical properties of any particular kind of wood from a study of its microscopic anatomy, this examination will give no clue

9

as to its susceptibility to fungal decay. The structure of the wood does, however, determine its porosity, and its ability to absorb preservative fluids, such as creosote. It will, of course, be more or less impossible for a fluid to penetrate into a timber if all its pores are blocked, or choked up. The sapwood of any living tree must obviously be freely permeable for the passage of the sap, and sapwood generally remains quite permeable even after the tree has been felled and the timber seasoned.

Only in a few trees does the wood remain equally permeable after its transformation into heartwood. Not only do the cells tend to become filled with gum and other resinous materials, but also the vessels are frequently plugged with tyloses. These are bladder-like outgrowths from the thin-walled parenchyma cells adjacent to the vessels. It is the presence of these tyloses which makes English Oak heartwood so impervious to liquids, and thereby render it the ideal wood for the construction of barrels and vats. Not all Oaks, however, form tyloses in the heartwood ; that of the American " red " Oak groups, for instance, remains quite porous. It is easy to test the porosity of a strip of Oak wood by blowing air through the vessels into water.

CHEMISTRY OF WOOD

Although the chemical composition of wood has been the subject of intensive research in many countries it is not yet fully understood.

Wood contains an intimate mixture of many different chemical compounds which are conveniently classified into:

(a) Those which go to build up cell walls, and can be regarded as forming the basic wood substance; and

(b) The more or less extraneous materials contained in the cell cavities, or which have infiltrated into the cell walls. Such

10

materials can generally be extracted from the wood by boiling it in water, or in solvents such as alcohol or benzene, and they are therefore referred to as " extractives ".

(a) *Basic Wood Substance*

The basic wood substance consists principally of *cellulose*, which occurs in a more or less pure form in cotton and linen; and *lignin*, which is never found in a pure state in nature; together with a lesser proportion of various polysaccharides known as *hemicelluloses*.

Cellulose, which has been called the " Noble Molecule ", is formed in the plant by polymerization from glucose units with loss of water. It is now an industrial raw material of the greatest importance. Enormous quantities of cellulose are prepared annually from softwoods in Scandinavia and America. These are used in the manufacture of rayon, transparent sheet (cellophane), synthetic finishes, and many other organic chemicals. The cellulose molecule has a long chain structure which confers great tensile strength on any materials of which it forms a part. Pure cellulose can be decomposed by many different fungi, but when it occurs in intimate mixture with lignin, as in wood, it is much more resistant, and only certain fungi are then able to break it down.

The composition of lignin remains somewhat of an enigma for the wood chemist. After extraction from the wood by chemicals it appears as a brown powder, but while still in the wood it is probably colourless. It gives certain characteristic reactions, such as turning bright red on treatment with phloroglucin and strong hydrochloric acid, but it is, on the whole, an inert substance for which few industrial uses have been found. Vast quantities of lignin are produced annually during the manufacture of cellulose, and many teams of research workers are endeavouring to discover profitable uses for it. Lignin is relatively resistant to decomposition by micro-organisms, and

11

the humus in soil is largely composed of lignin residues derived from plant remains from which the cellulose has been rotted away. Some of the higher fungi can decompose lignin, but few can utilize it as their sole source of energy. Lignin is not distributed evenly throughout the cell walls of the wood, certain layers being more highly lignified than others; for this reason one sometimes finds certain elements of the wood are attacked before others.

Both in softwoods and in hardwoods the basic wood substance remains fairly constant in composition. The cellulose content varies between 50 per cent and 60 per cent, and the lignin between 20 per cent and 28 per cent of its dry weight; the latter tending to be rather higher in tropical woods than in those grown in a temperate climate. The hemicelluloses may amount to 10 per cent or more, and tend to occur in greater amounts in hardwoods than in softwoods.

(b) *Extractives*

The extractives are of three main types:

(1) Food materials stored in cells, such as sugars, soluble starches and the like.

(2) Extractives toxic to fungi which act as natural preservatives for the wood, such as tannin and certain complicated phenolic compounds, some of which have a strong antibiotic action towards micro-organisms.

(3) Mineral salts.

DURABILITY OF WOODS

Since the basic wood substance varies but little in chemical composition from one kind of tree to another, the differences in durability that exist between species must be due either to variations in density (i.e. to differences in the amount of the wood substance present) or to differences in the nature and amount of the extractives present.

While it is true that many of the most durable woods are hard and heavy, there are also a number of light-weight woods which are very durable. Many experiments have been carried out to discover whether there is any correlation between density and durability, and the results of these have shown that, in general, density is a poor guide to durability.

It is usually possible to extract from any durable timber substances which are in some degree toxic or poisonous to wood-rotting fungi, and it is now generally agreed that it is the presence of these natural preservatives in the heartwood of durable timbers which renders them resistant to fungal decay. Many of the compounds which occur in the heartwood of Pines and Cedars have now been isolated and identified chemically, and some of them have been shown to be as toxic to fungi as mercuric chloride (corrosive sublimate). Though resin is not appreciably toxic to wood-rotting fungi, it does, if present in sufficient quantities, increase the resistance of wood to decay. This is probably due to the physical protection it affords to the wood substances which are, as it were, screened from the ferments of the fungi.

Much work still remains to be done before the chemistry of the heartwood substances and extractives of the durable hardwoods is fully understood, but a start has been made, and a number of interesting antibiotics have already been isolated from timbers, and their toxicity to micro-organisms tested.

Wood contains a certain amount of mineral matter, and formerly wood ash was an important source of potash. It is still used in horticulture as a fertilizer to enrich soils with the minerals necessary for plant growth. The mineral content of wood appears always to be adequate for the organisms which grow on it.

The nitrogen content of wood is low, varying between 0.05 per cent and 0.5 per cent of its dry weight, and it has been shown that the addition of nitrogenous materials to wood increases its susceptibility to decay by fungi.

Fungal decay is often followed by insect attack, and, in fact, many kinds of insects attack only wood that is partially decayed. It is probable that the softer condition of the decayed wood is one of the principal reasons why it is much more readily attacked, but it is also possible that decayed wood is intrinsically more nourishing than sound wood for certain insects.

Durability Classification

In speaking of the natural durability of timbers it is always the durability of the heartwood that is implied, as, with few exceptions, the sapwood has always a low resistance to fungal attack after the tree has been felled. In the species where there is no well-defined heartwood there is little difference in the decay resistance of the inner and the outer wood. Great variation in durability can be found in different samples of the same species of tree, depending on the conditions under which the tree was grown, and on its age. Even within a single log there may be a difference between the inner and the outer zones of the heartwood, and between the butt and the upper part of the trunk. In many trees, as for instance African Mahogany and Western Red Cedar, the wood from the outer rings of the heartwood is more resistant to decay than is that which comes from nearer the pith. No precise classification of timbers on a basis of their durability is therefore possible, and one can only classify them into a number of broad groups, as follows:

Very Durable: Timbers that are almost immune to fungal

attack and which can be expected to last for a great many years, even when used in contact with the ground, or under other permanently damp conditions. Timbers in this class may be used with confidence for transmission poles; railway sleepers; bridging timbers; marine piling; foundation timbers; hop poles; and fencing.

Durable : These timbers will decay when exposed to conditions favourable to fungal attack, but only very slowly. They can safely be used for the exposed parts of permanent structures that are not in direct contact with the soil. They are suitable for the frames, keels, and decking of boats; for the making of vats; for window sills; and for domestic draining boards.

Moderately Durable : These timbers should never be used in direct contact with the soil unless they have been given preservative treatment; but they will not decay rapidly if exposed to conditions which are only intermittently damp. They can safely be used for those parts of permanent structures that are given protection against the weather, such as rafters and joists. They can be used in vehicles and for some parts of boats.

Not Durable : Timbers that decay fairly rapidly in contact with the ground, and which should always be given preservative treatment if there is any risk of their being exposed to damp conditions.

Perishable : Timbers thus described require rapid extraction from the forest after felling, and immediate conversion and drying, to avoid decay in the log stage or during seasoning. They should always receive preservative treatment if used for permanent constructional work.

TABLE 1. *Classification of timbers on basis of durability of their heartwood*

Very Durable	Durable	Moderately Durable	Non-durable	Perish-able
Softwoods				
Sequoia	Kauri	Douglas Fir	Hem-lock	Sap-wood of pines
Yew	Pitch Pine	Larch	Silver Fir	
	(best grades)	Maritime Pine	Spruces	
	Western Red Cedar	Redwood (Baltic) Scots Pine Yellow Pine		
Hardwoods				
Afrormosia Afzelia	Agba Chestnut (sweet)	Crabwood	Abura	Alder
Albizzia Black Cabbage Bark	Guarea Idigbo	Dahoma Danta Gurjun	Ash Elm Gaboon	Balsa Beech Horse Chest-nut
Curupay Greenheart	Kempas Mahogany (American)	Karri Keruing (Malayan)	Obeche Poplar (grey)	Ilomba Lime
Iroko	Meranti (red)	Mahogany (African)	Ramin	
Jarrah	Mora	Niangon	Seraya (white)	Plane Willows
Kapur Makore	Oak (English) Oak (Ameri-can white)	Oak (Turkey) Oak (Ameri-can red)		
Muninga Okan	Robinia Santa Maria	Sapele Walnut (European)		
Opepe	S. American Cedar			
Padauk Rhodesian 'Teak' Tallow-wood Teak Turpentine Wallaba	Utile			

ASSESSMENT OF NATURAL DURABILITY

The resistance of timbers to fungal decay can be assessed by observing how long stakes of a standard size will last when partially buried in soil. At the Forest Products Research Laboratory at Princes Risborough, and in other research establishments, large numbers of stakes have been set in the ground and examined each year, until they failed when struck with a standard mallet. It is obviously necessary with this method to wait many years before the more durable species show differences, and so a rapid laboratory method for measuring resistance to fungal decay has been developed. The method is as follows:

Small test pieces are taken from various parts of the trunk of a tree, selected so as to obtain as fair sampling as possible. These are exposed, at a constant temperature, to pure cultures of various wood-rotting fungi. After four months exposure to the fungal attack they are examined and any loss in dry weight they may have suffered is determined. This figure, expressed as a percentage of the original dry weight of the sample, gives a useful measure of the susceptibility of the wood to decay.

Both field and laboratory tests have been carried out on a wide range of timbers so that it is now possible to relate the two sets of figures for the various classes of durability, as follows.

Durability Class.	Life of 2×2 in. stake in soil, in England.	Average loss in dry weight % in laboratory tests
Very Durable	Over 25 years	Nil or negligible
Durable	15-25 years	Up to 5
Moderately Durable	10-15 years	5-10
Non-durable	5-10 years	10-30
Perishable	less than 5 years	Over 30

17

The durability of specimens of larger cross-sections cannot be deduced precisely from the above figures. Generally speaking an increase in cross-section does not proportionally increase the life of the more perishable timbers. With durable timbers, however, the increase in life will probably be more than proportional to the increase in thickness.

RESISTANCE TO INSECT ATTACK

Although it is true that most of the timbers which are highly resistant to fungal attack are also resistant to wood-boring insects, it must not be assumed that this will invariably be the case. The resistance of many tropical timbers to Termites has been established as the result of field tests, but there is little precise information as yet as to the resistance of timbers to the other wood-borers.

In temperate countries there are very few wood-boring insects that will attack sound heartwood of any of the timbers in which it is clearly defined. The Common Furniture Beetle—*Anobium punctatum*—for instance, rarely, if ever, attacks sound heartwood of Pine or Oak. Powder-post Beetles—*Lyctus* spp.—infest only the sapwood of hardwoods, such as Oak, Ash, Walnut, etc., as these insects derive their nourishment from starch which is present only in sapwood. Generally speaking it is the proportion of sapwood in a commercial sample of timber that determines its susceptibility to attack by any insects other than Termites.

CHAPTER 3

Causes of Deterioration in Timber

TIMBER does not deteriorate as a result of ageing alone, as do some other organic materials such as rubber. There is no such thing as timber " losing its nature " by the mere passage of time. Kept under the proper conditions wood is an exceptionally durable material, and wooden objects have been recovered from the Egyptian tombs thousands of years old, but still in a perfect state of preservation. Even in our own damp climate there are many wooden roofs that have stood for centuries without suffering the least deterioration; and our homes and museums contain innumerable pieces of furniture, hundreds of years old, which are as strong and serviceable today as on the day they were made. The violins of Stradivarius (*circa* 1700) vibrate today as truly as, and even more sweetly than, when the master's hand first fashioned them. Timber does not become " tired " and suffer " fatigue " as many metals do after repeated exposure to stresses, and its acoustic properties do not appear to change with time and usage.

But if timber is exposed to persistently damp conditions it will, sooner or later, assuredly become decayed; and if woodborers are allowed to infest it they will attack it and reduce it to powder, in time depending on the kind of wood. It is the purpose of this book to describe the various forms of deterioration which timber can suffer and to suggest how they can be recognized and prevented. By understanding the conditions under which the destructive agencies work users of timber can take steps to safeguard woodwork from their attack, and thereby extend the life of any wooden structure almost indefinitely.

The destructive agencies that attack wood can be classified as follows:

(1) Mechanical wear.
(2) Decomposition by fire or prolonged heating.
(3) Chemical attack.
(4) Fungal decay.
(5) Insect attack.
(6) Attack by other animals, marine borers, birds, etc.

Of these, fungal decay and insect attack are of outstanding importance and are dealt with fully in succeeding chapters. The characteristic features of each form of attack are tabulated below for easy reference.

(1) MECHANICAL WEAR

The effects of ordinary wear can usually be recognized without much difficulty as they are confined to exposed surfaces, but occasionally they are mistaken for decay. For instance, if softwood flooring blocks are sawn so that the wearing surface is more or less parallel to the annual rings and not at right angles to them (i.e. if the timber is " slash sawn " and not "quarter or rift sawn") the surface will splinter and the annual rings shell away in a manner somewhat suggestive of fungal decay. Again, the dust formed by friction between the runners of drawers and their guides is sometimes mistaken for the dust formed by wood-boring beetles. When there is any doubt as to the cause of the breakdown, microscopic examination of the wood should be made.

While timber's resistance to wear varies greatly from species to species, depending on its density and structure, it is possible to improve the wearing qualities of timber surfaces by treating them with suitable polishes or varnishes, or by coating them with a film of paint. Regular treatment of flooring with preparations containing linseed oil or a suitable wax, will greatly prolong its life, provided the traffic is only moderately heavy, and this will also reduce the tendency of the fibres on the surface to become separated and powder away. Wherever possible washing and scrubbing of wooden floors should be avoided as constant wetting of the surface tends to raise the grain of the wood and to render is soft and "woolly". There is also the risk that the floor may become so damp that conditions suitable for fungal decay may be set up.

(2) Decomposition by Heat

If the temperature of wood is raised sufficiently high in the presence of oxygen it will ignite and burn. There is considerable variation between timbers in the ease with which they can be ignited—everyone knows that it is easier to light a fire with softwood kindling than with elm sticks—but the degree of dryness of the wood is the most important factor affecting the inflammability. No treatment can render wood truly fireproof since if its temperature is raised above a certain point, e.g. between 400 and 500°F, so-called "destructive distillation" of the wood occurs even in the absence of oxygen, and most untreated timbers ignite in air at about 460°F. If wood is heated in a chamber from which air is excluded inflammable gases are given off and the wood becomes carbonized and turns into charcoal. Even at temperatures well below those at which ignition and destructive distillation immediately take place prolonged exposure may bring about profound changes.

It is likely that wood will undergo some slow chemical change if it is exposed for any considerable time to temperatures at, or only slightly above, the boiling point of water. Timber that has been in close proximity to steam-heating

C

pipes, or which has formed part of a drying kiln or steaming chest, may, after years, show a form of decomposition that closely resembles fungal decay, the wood becoming dark brown and crumbly and cracking up into square-edged rectangular pieces. It may, in fact, be difficult, without microscopic examination, to distinguish between decomposition caused by prolonged heating and that brought about by fungi; but if the origin of the specimen be known the cause can usually be surmised since fungal decay cannot occur at temperatures above about 45°C (= 112°F). The risk of thermal decomposition can be minimized by providing some insulation between the source of heat and the timber. The provision of such insulation between timber panelling and heating pipes and radiators is always desirable, as the heat will, in any case, dry out the timber so much that it will shrink excessively and develop unsightly splits and cracks.

(3) CHEMICAL ATTACK

If wood comes into contact with certain chemicals such as strong acids or alkalis, some of its constituents may be decomposed and it may disintegrate. Wood that has been damaged by contact with a chemical often has a fuzzy, woolly appearance, owing to the individual fibres having become separated by dissolution of those substances which bind them together in the wood. (See Fig. 1.)

Except as a result of accidental spilling it is rare for wood to come into contact with strong chemicals in domestic buildings. Occasionally floors are damaged by continual washing with strong soda solutions. Water containing soda should never be used for washing bare woodwork. Nowadays there are plenty of excellent detergents on the market which can be used without any risk of harm to the floor. Damage has been caused

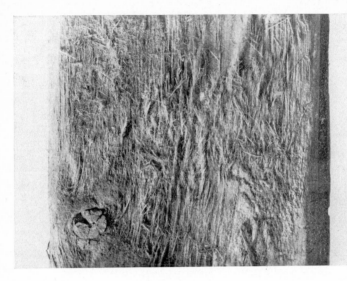

Fig. 1. Wood defibrated as a result of chemical action. C.C.R.

by strong acids or alkalis that had been misguidedly used to sterilize woodwork suspected of infection with dry rot.

An unusual instance of chemical breakdown occurred in the floor of a dance hall on which had been laid hornbeam blocks dyed black. Soon after the floor had been constructed the surface began to crumble away, and dancing produced a fine black powder that settled on shoes and stockings. This was discovered to be the result of the wood being decomposed by the action of the black dye which had a strongly acid reaction. No surface treatment could cure the condition and the floor had to be relaid. No dye should ever be used for colouring wood unless it is first ascertained to be harmless to timber.

One of the most surprising cases of damage caused by acids was the discovery of woodwork *inside* a piano which had been decomposed by the action of sulphuric acid. No one

23

knew how it had got there, and the only explanation offered was that someone had accidentally spilt the contents of an accumulator inside the piano!

Woodwork that has been exposed for long periods to fumes from a coke-burning stove sometimes suffers damage. The sulphur dioxide is absorbed by the wood, and accumulates until the concentration is sufficiently high to cause breakdown. This is most likely to occur in such places as the roof of an engine-shed where the wood is also exposed to rather high temperatures. The surface layers of roofing timbers in cities where the air normally contains a relatively high concentration of sulphur dioxide may become brittle and friable to a depth of an eighth of an inch or so, but such disintegration will remain more or less superficial. Ordinary wood preservatives do not protect timber against chemical attack, so when it is known that woodwork may be exposed to acid fumes it should receive a good coating of an acid-resisting paint.

Floors on which chemicals in bags have been stored sometimes show signs of damage, which may be due to certain impurities being present in otherwise innocuous chemicals. Contamination with common salt does not cause any breakdown of the wood but it does render the wood hygroscopic, so that whenever the air becomes humid any wood containing salt becomes damp. Often the floor under a water softener becomes contaminated with salt spilt when recharging the softener. Once floor boards have become impregnated with salt it is very difficult to get rid of it even by repeated washing, so care should be taken not to spill solid salt or briny water on wooden floors. Timber that has been impregnated with sea water will always become damp in humid weather owing to the hygroscopicity of the salt.

In dye houses, and in certain other types of chemical plant, wooden vats are used to contain solutions that may be corrosive; it is therefore important that these should be constructed of a timber which is naturally resistant to decomposition. Southern cypress used to be the favourite wood for this purpose but supplies of this are no longer available in this country. Choice should therefore be made from such woods as Douglas Fir, Pitch Pine, or one of the dense hardwoods such as Purpleheart, Greenheart or Afzelia. Resistant hardwoods should also be used for the floors of factories if there is any risk of caustic or corrosive chemicals being spilt.

(4) Fungal Decay

If wood is kept in a damp condition for any length of time it becomes infected with wood-rotting fungi which bring about its decomposition, more or less rapidly according to the species of fungus and the kind of wood.

The nature of fungal decay and the conditions under which

Fig. 2. Fungal decay caused by Dry Rot Fungus.

it occurs are fully discussed in Chapter 4, but it is convenient at this point to list the features by which such decay can be recognized and distinguished from other forms of attack. When rot has reached an advanced stage it is usually quite easy to decide if it has been due to fungal attack, especially if there are some fungus growths present. (See Fig. 2). But in an early stage of the attack, or when the decay is mainly internal, there maybe no signs of fungi, and the cause of the rot may not be obvious. It must be emphasized that the outward appearance of decay in any wood depends, not only on the species of fungus involved, but also upon the stage to which the attack has progressed; the first, or incipient, stage often being quite different from the final stages. The term "dote" is frequently used by practical timber men to mean incipient decay which has not yet turned into clearly recognizable rot.

By some or all of the following symptoms fungal decay may be recognized:

Change in Colour: Wood attacked by wood-rotting fungi becomes either lighter or darker than its normal colour. In standing trees the first indication of unsoundness is often the appearance of dark brown, or purplish coloured streaks in the heartwood. Such discoloration often surrounds the area in which there is obvious rot. In felled or sawn hardwoods, such as Beech and Ash, the appearance of pale cream, or whitish spots is frequently the first indication of dote; while in softwoods decay more often produces brownish spots or streaks. Care must be taken not to mistake for incipient decay the greyish blue sap-stain, or "blue stain", which is caused by the growth through the sapwood of virtually harmless moulds. (See Chapter 5.)

Loss of Strength and Softening: Fungal decay soon causes wood to become softer and to lose its mechanical strength. If decay is suspected the discoloured area should be probed with a pointed tool and its resistance compared with that of obviously sound wood. Again, in a sound piece of softwood it is possible to prize up a splinter if the tip of a knife is inserted and the fibres slowly raised, whereas if incipient decay is present the fibres will break off short over the tip of the knife.

The toughness of wood is quickly reduced by fungal attack, and if a piece of wood breaks with a short carroty fracture when struck against a hard surface the presence of decay must be suspected.

There has been considerable interest in the possibility of developing non-destructive methods of testing which would reveal the presence of defects (including decay) that lower the strength of the wood. One such method is by measuring the changes in resonance frequency induced by compression waves, which diminishes as decay proceeds. An ultra-sonic pulse technique has been used by Lee* to measure the transmission of energy in sound and decayed timber. Using a commercial flaw detector Waid and Woodman† found that decay greatly reduced the energy transmitted through wood and suggested that this technique could be used to detect the presence of butt rot in standing trees, as well as deep seated defects in sawn timber. Lee measured the transmission of ultrasonic pulses through large beams infected with dry rot or wood-boring beetles to estimate the effective loss in load bearing cross section but found it difficult to attach the probes smoothly enough to the wood.

Loss in Weight: Any sample of wood which is abnormally light in weight will probably be found to be unsound. It must however be remembered in this connection that woods normally vary considerably in density, depending on the rate at which

---

* LEE, I. D. G., *J. Inst. Wood Science* **3,** 21, (1959).
† WAID, J. S. and WOODMAN, N. S., *Nature* **180,** 47, (1957).

the tree has grown, and that samples which are perfectly sound may sometimes be found to have densities considerably below the average. The amount of moisture in wood also, of course, greatly affects its apparent density, and comparison must be made with wood at approximately the same moisture content.

Change in Odour: Sound, healthy softwood has a pleasant, fresh, resinous smell, while decayed wood usually has a "mushroomy" and stale odour. When one is testing the soundness of a beam by boring into it, it is helpful to smell the borings from each depth, as well as to test them with the fingers. The presence of a musty, mouldy smell, though indicative of damp conditions favourable to the growth of all kinds of fungus, does not necessarily indicate the presence of dry rot.

Increase in Permeability of Wood: Wood that is infected with decay absorbs fluids much more readily than sound wood. If one wets the surface of a board in which there are spots of decay these will instantly become more obvious, as the fluid soaks quickly into the places where the wood is decayed, making it darker in that area than the surrounding healthy wood which absorbs the liquid more slowly. Methylated spirits give a quicker result than water, but the wood should be examined immediately after the fluid is applied as the differences in colour soon become less pronounced. This test is particularly useful for the detection of incipient decay on the surface of planed softwood boards.

Increase in Inflammability: Decayed wood is more easily ignited than sound wood. It will be remembered that very rotten wood was at one time used as tinder.

(5) INSECT ATTACK

Damage by wood-boring insects can usually be recognized without difficulty. The larvæ (grubs) bore through the wood forming a network of tunnels, which are often filled with wood dust (known as "frass"). Piles of this dust, on or beneath infected wood, are a sure indication that living insects are present and working actively. After the beetles have emerged from the wood in which, as larvae, they have completed their development, the small, round exit holes will be found on the exposed surfaces of the wood. These holes vary in size according to the species of the insect.

The damage caused by Termites—White Ants—(See Chapter 7.) is different from that caused by most other insects; but these pests do not occur in Northern Europe so their presence need not be suspected in wood from this area. Termites work inside pieces of wood, excavating large tunnels and galleries, sometimes hollowing out the wood completely. They never form exit holes on the surface of the wood which they most carefully avoid damaging.

Insect attack is often confined to the sapwood, and it is not uncommon to find that the sapwood of rafters in old buildings has disintegrated completely, while the heartwood has remained untouched.

Insect attack and fungal decay are frequently found together in the same piece of wood. Many insects live only in partially decayed wood, and others, such as the Death-Watch Beetle, show a distinct preference for wood that has been softened by fungal decay.

(6) Attack by Other Animals

Marine Borers

As their name implies, they attack timber only in sea water. In this country there are no animals that cause serious damage to timber submerged in fresh water. Damage by Marine Borers is therefore evidence that the wood in question has been submerged in salt or brackish water.

The Shipworm bores deeply into wood, forming tunnels about 1/4 in. across, and lined with a shell-like material which has a nacreous lustre.

The Gribble makes smaller burrows, only a tenth to a twentieth of an inch in diameter, and which are usually confined to within 1/2 in. of the exposed surface of the wood.

Woodpeckers

These birds normally confine their attention to partially rotten trees in which they search for the grubs of wood-inhabiting insects, and in which they excavate holes for their nests. Occasionally, for no obvious reason, a Woodpecker will attack a sound pole, even a thoroughly creosoted telegraph pole, and when once the bird has got in the habit of attacking that particular pole it will continue to do so in spite of efforts to discourage it. Sometimes a bird will make a dozen or more holes, two or three inches in diameter and several inches deep, into the same pole. The only certain way of protecting such a pole is to bind round it fine gauge wire netting. The theory has been put forward that the humming of the wires attached to the pole suggests to the bird that the pole is alive with insects! Scientific evidence in support of this theory is scanty, but it does seem to be a fact that poles which carry live wires are more often attacked than those which do not. The provision of nesting boxes at intervals along a line of poles is said to reduce the risk of damage.

TABLE 2. *Characteristic Features of Various Forms of Timber Deterioration*

	Fungal decay	Insect attack	Marine Borers	Heat	Chemical attack	Mechanical wear
Occurrence:	Damp situations in buildings or outdoors.	Dry or damp situations.	Only in sea or brackish water.	In buildings near heating appliances, etc.	In factories where chemicals are used, and in buildings where acid fumes are present.	Exposed surfaces, e.g. flooring.
Appearance:	Wood softened, discoloured, often cracked up, sometimes with lens-shaped cavities.	Wood tunnelled and powdery, often with round exit holes on surface.	Wood tunnelled and or chewed away on the surface.	Wood darkened, sometimes cracked up.	Wood defibrated into lint-like material consisting of separate fibres.	Surface disintegrated. Powdered wood often tends to shell away.
Other Features:	Growths of fungi, e.g. toadstools or skins, may be present but these are often absent.	Larvae (worms) present in the tunnels. Possibly beetles on the surface.	"Worms" or crustaceans may be present in the wood.	None.	Reaction of wood may be abnormal, e.g. strongly acid or alkaline.	None.

31

CHAPTER 4

Fungal Decay

WOOD, as already explained, does not decay merely as a result of exposure to moist conditions; nor does it lose its nature by being kept in an exceedingly dry atmosphere. Decay is the result of fungal attack, which leads to the breakdown and ultimate dissolution of the wood substance.

The true nature of decay remained a mystery until about a century ago. Though the presence of fungi had long been associated with the decay of wood and other materials, the fungi themselves were supposed to be "generated" by the processes of decomposition. Ambrose Bowden, for instance, writing in 1815, was convinced that decay in ships' timbers was due to "vegetation of the sap excited by the action of heat". Sowerby, the famous botanist, however, evidently appreciated that there was some close connection between the presence of fungi and the development of rot, and when he was asked by the Admiralty, in 1821, to study the problem of decay in the wooden warships, listed a score or more species of fungi in his report. Perhaps it was Benjamin Johnson who was the first to realize the true role fungi play in causing rot, for in 1803 he stated categorically in a communication to the Society for the Encouragement of the Arts, Manufactures and Commerce (now the Royal Society of Arts) that dry rot is the result of a "visit from a plant, and always is and ever was so". Theodore Hartig in 1833 recognized the close association between fungi and rot in wood, but thought that the fungus threads developed spontaneously, and then, by their "vegetation", accelerated the process of decomposition. It was his son, Robert Hartig, who proved that fungi are the cause and not the result of rot in trees and timber. His brilliant work dominated thought on this subject till the end of last century, and his excellent illustrations were copied again and again.

Since fungi play such an important role in bringing about timber decay, it is necessary to understand what kind of organisms they are, how they are reproduced, and the conditions under which they can grow and flourish. The study of fungi is called mycology and those who undertake it are called mycologists.

Nature of Fungi

Fungi are generally regarded as a highly specialized class of plants, though there are some mycologists who would consider them as belonging to a phylum (kingdom) of their own, comparable to that of plants and animals. The relationship of fungi to other plants is in a way similar to that of insects to other animals. Both groups exhibit a great diversity of form, are exceedingly numerous both in numbers and species, and have the means for incredibly rapid multiplication; and both are responsible for many of the diseases suffered by other plants and animals.

Fungi differ fundamentally from all the green plants which live by the process known as photosynthesis. No fungi possess chlorophyll (the green colouring matter which is in leaves) and they are therefore unable to build up sugar and starch from the carbon dioxide in the atmosphere. Fungi, like animals, must find ready-make organic food materials on which to live. The variety of materials on which they will grow is surprising. Practically any material obtained from plants or animals can provide sustenance for some species of fungus. Even such resistant materials as cork and hair can be attacked, and many man-made products, such as nitrocellulose, can be decomposed by fungi.

Structure and Reproduction of Fungi

Fungi are reproduced by bodies known as " spores ", which correspond to the seeds of higher plants, but which are very much smaller, and are usually reproduced in very large numbers. The spores of most fungi consist of a single cell and measure only 5-10 microns in length. A micron is one thousandth of a millimetre, and is represented by the Greek letter μ.

In other terms, their length varies from 2 to 5 ten-thousandths of an inch. A few fungi form longer, multicellular spores, but the size even of these is much less than that of the smallest true seed. Spores are formed in many different ways, and it is on the structure of the spore-bearing organs that the classification of fungi is based.

If the spores of fungi fall on a suitable substratum they germinate when moistened, as do the seeds of the higher plants. The spore wall bursts and a germ tube grows out. This germ tube elongates by apical growth and becomes a *hypha*. The hypha then branches and the resulting weft of hyphæ begins to permeate the substratum, be it soil, compost or timber, or, if the fungus be a parasitic one, the living tissues of a leaf, stem or fruit, or even, in the case of a pathogenic organism, the skin or tissues of an animal. The weft of tissue formed by fungal hyphæ is known as *mycelium*, or spawn. This mycelium may become matted to form thick sheets, or aggregated into root-like strands, or *rhizomorphs* (from the Greek words meaning "having the shape of a root").

After a fungus has built up a sufficient mass of mycelium it usually proceeds to form a fruit body on which fresh spores will be borne and the life cycle completed. Although some of these fructifications are large and complicated structures they are all formed by the interweaving of microscopic hyphæ, many of which become highly specialized and have conducting or skeletal functions. As a rough analogy one may compare a fungus structure to a complicated piece of knitting or weaving; in a contrast to the tissue formation of a green plant, which could be likened to brickwork built up of numerous individual cells.

The fructification, or fruit body, which is sometimes called a sporophore (spore bearer), is usually formed on the external surface of the substratum, thus allowing the spores to be discharged into the air. Often the mushroom in the grass or the bracket-like growth on the tree is the only indication to the casual observer that fungi exist, as the whole of the vegetative mycelium, or spawn, is hidden under the turf or in the trunk of the tree. Removal of the fructification no more checks the growth of the fungus than plucking fruit checks the growth of a tree. The shape, size and texture of the fruit body vary according to the species of the fungus concerned, and the only means of classifying fungi and determining the species is by examination of these sporophores. They may vary in size from minute structures smaller than a pin's head up to huge growths several feet in diameter. Most wood-rotting fungi form fructifications which are easily visible and of appreciable size.

Classification of Fungi

Many important wood-destroying-fungi belong to the group known as *Basidiomycetes*. These bear their spores on a structure called the *basidium*. (See Fig. 3.) Normally four spores are formed on each basidium, being produced at the end of short stalks from which they are violently discharged when ripe. The basidia are usually formed in a compact superficial layer called the *hymenium*. The Basidiomycetes are subdivided according to the way this hymenium is borne and displayed.

35

Most of the wood-rotting fungi in this group belong to one or other of four families:

Thelephoraceæ. Hymenium freely exposed on a flat skin-like surface.

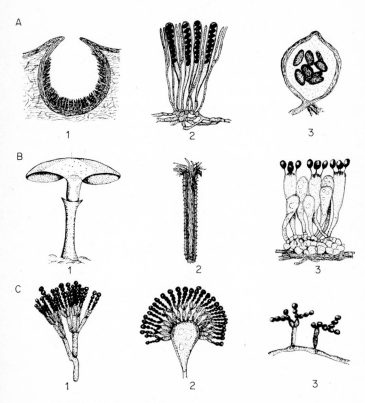

Fig. 3. Fruiting structures of fungi. A. *Ascomycetes* (1) Embedded perithecium. (2) Asci with eight spores. (3) Another type of ascus. B. *Basidiomycetes* (Agaric) (1) Sporophore. (2) Section of gill. (3) Basidia carrying four spores each. C. *Fungi imperfecti.* (1) *Penicillium.* (2) *Aspergillus.* (3) *Hormodendron.* A1 and B2 magnified. A2 and 3, B3, and C1, 2 and 3 very highly magnified.

Hydnaceæ. Hymenium borne on spines, or projections, pointing downwards on the underside of the fructification.

Agaricaceæ. Hymenium covers the surface of radiating plate-like gills underneath a cap (pileus) supported on a stem.

Polyporaceæ. Hymenium develops on the inside of small tubes or pores usually on the underside of a bracket. Many of the fungi in this group form thick woody growths that persist for years on the trunks or stumps of trees.

Fungi capable of decomposing wood also occur in another large group of the higher fungi known as the *Ascomycetes.* In these fungi the spores are formed inside a club-shaped bag known as an *ascus.* When these asci are ripe they discharge their spores violently for a short distance into the air. Most of the fungi which cause the troublesome dark stains in light-coloured woods belong to this group. (See Chapter 5.) Many *Ascomycetes* produce more than one type of spore, as, in addition to ascopores, they often possess what is called an "imperfect" stage in which various secondary spores are formed. These may be regarded as a means of vegetative propagation. All those species of fungi which, so far as is known, are reproduced only in this way (i.e. by means of asexual secondary spores) or by the fragmentation of hyphæ, belong to a large group known as the *Fungi Imperfecti.* The majority of the micro-fungi commonly known as moulds belong to this group.

Reproductive Power of Fungi

Fungi are able to reproduce themselves with extraordinary rapidity for they can produce fantastic numbers of spores in a very short time. One has only to observe the rate at which blight can spread in a field of potatoes, or "rust" in a corn crop, to appreciate the rapidity of reproduction possessed by these parasites. It has been estimated that a fruit body of the dry-rot fungus one yard square can produce fifty million spores a minute over a period of many days. When several fruit bodies of this fungus are present in a room it is not uncommon to find every object in the room covered with a thick layer of spore dust totalling countless millions in all. Some of the larger woody fungi that grow on trees have been estimated to produce up to nine hundred million spores per hour over periods of weeks, or even months. Fungus spores being very light can remain suspended in the air, and may drift for long distances (they have, for instance, been trapped on aircraft miles high in the sky) so that there is obviously a very good chance of any suitable habitat sooner or later becoming infected and colonized. In practice, this means that any piece of wood that remains in a moist condition will in time certainly become infected by wood-rotting fungi and start to decay.

Whether or not timber decays depends largely on the conditions to which it is exposed, and whether these are suitable for fungal growth. It is therefore important to know under what conditions fungi flourish—in other words, we must know something about their physiology.

For a fungus to develop the following conditions must exist:

(1) There must be a source of infection. We have already seen how widespread fungal infection can be in the form of air-borne spores.

(2) A suitable substratum must be present on which the spores can germinate, and from which the fungus can derive its nourishment.

(3) Moisture must be present in sufficient amount to permit the spores to germinate and growth to develop.

(4) Oxygen must be available. Fungi are aerobic organisms— that is to say they require oxygen for their life processes and respiration. Generally fungi grow only in the presence

of air but some species can grow under water if the latter contains dissolved oxygen.

(5) The temperature must be suitable for growth of the fungi.

Let us consider these requirements in more detail.

(1) *Source of Infection.* Most soils contain quantities of organic matter in which many different kinds of organisms, both fungal and bacterial, are growing. It is therefore possible for infection to spread directly by hyphae growing from the soil on to the timber. In a mine fungal growths may spread over the surface of the coal or rock from one pit prop to another; while in a building it is possible for the strands of the Dry Rot Fungus to pass over, and even through, brickwork, from one piece of wood to another. If unseasoned boards are piled closely together fungus growths can spread out from an infected piece and infect other pieces in contact with it. In medical terms decay can be contagious as well as infectious.

(2) *Suitable Substratum.* The normal substratum for wood-rotting fungi is obviously wood; but it must be remembreed that there are thousands of different kinds of wood and that all kinds are not equally suitable for all kinds of fungus. There are some fungi, such as the Cellar Fungus, that can grow on a wide variety of timbers and will attack the wood of both conifers and broad-leaved trees. However, generally speaking, coniferous timbers are attacked by one group of fungi, and hardwoods by another. Many naturally durable woods which contain substances toxic to most fungi can be attacked only by certain specialized species. These species are indifferent, or resistant, to those particular chemicals to which the timber owes its natural durability and its immunity from attack by other fungi. It has been found, for instance, that the Beef-steak Fungus, which is normally found only on Oak trees and Sweet Chestnut,

can tolerate concentrations of oak tannin that will kill the Dry Rot Fungus which is typically an inhabitant of softwoods.

The fungi that attack standing trees tend to be more specialized than those which grow on fallen logs and sawn timber. Many trees are attacked only by certain parasites which may occur only on that particular species of tree or its close relations. For instance the Birch Polypore is by far the commonest fungus found on Birch in this country and it is rarely found on any other tree.

Wood-rotting fungi can infect other materials containing cellulose, particularly those that are derived from wood, such as paper. It is not uncommon to find books and papers in a library attacked by Dry Rot Fungus which has spread from decayed shelving.

Many wood-destroying fungi can live in, and grow through, earth, particularly if it contains woody residues. Sometimes the soil underneath a house which has been infected by dry rot becomes contaminated with the strands of the fungus, and these may grow up and re-infect the new floors if the soil is not effectively sterilized when repairs are carried out.

It is possible to poison the food material of a fungus by treating it with a fungicide and this to render it immune to attack. This is the basis of the preservation of wood by chemical treatment.

(3) *Moisture Requirements.* In practice, moisture content is by far the most important factor controlling the development of fungi on timber, and also on many other organic products. Fungi can develop on such materials only when they contain sufficient moisture. For the germination of the spores it is generally necessary not only for the substratum to be moist, but also for the relative humidity of the surrounding atmosphere to be high. Timber, in common with many other organic materials such as grain, cloth, straw and paper, always contains

a certain proportion of moisture, unless it has come straight out of a drying oven, or a completely moisture-free atmosphere in a desiccator. The amount of moisture which it contains depends on the degree of saturation of the air, i.e. on the relative humidity of the surrounding atmosphere. For instance, furniture in a normally heated living-room with a relative humidity of, say, 45 per cent, may contain 12 per cent of moisture based on the oven dry weight of the wood. In a freshly felled log there may be almost as much water (by weight) as there is wood; in fact, the sapwood often contains more than its own weight of water, the heartwood being usually somewhat less wet.

Part of the moisture in freshly felled "green" timber is in the cell cavities—this is the so-called "free" water—the rest is absorbed in the cell walls themselves. Little or no drying occurs while timber is still in the log form, but when sawn timber is piled openly it begins to dry out and season. When all the free water has evaporated from the cell cavities, and the walls begin to dry out, the "fibre-saturation point" is said to have been reached. This point varies slightly from one kind of timber to another but generally lies between 27 per cent and 30 per cent of the oven dry weight. When the timber dries still further it becomes stiffer and harder and begins to shrink. By the ordinary process of air drying timber in the open it is seldom possible in Northern Europe to reduce the moisture content below about 18 per cent however long the timber is left to season. When timber is required to be dryer than this it is necessary to dry it out in a specially heated room or timber-drying kiln. For the manufacture of furniture it is desirable that the moisture of the wood should be down to about 12 per cent, since, if the wood is used in a much moister condition than this, excessive shrinking will occur when the manufactured article is brought into a heated room.

Wood-rotting Basidiomycete fungi flourish best in timber

containing between 35 per cent and 50 per cent moisture, the exact figure depending both on the species of fungus and the kind of wood. There is no exact upper limit of moisture content for the growth of fungi in wood. The critical point is reached when the cell spaces are completely filled with water, for then there is no air in the wood and fungal growth will be checked on this account. The denser the wood the fewer air spaces there are, and the less water is required to saturate it completely. The maximum moisture content for growth will therefore be lower in very heavy dense woods than in light porous ones. The actual size of the piece of wood also has some bearing on the degree of saturation that fungi will tolerate. Fungi can grow into thin pieces of wood which are in a saturated condition because some of their hyphæ remain in contact with the air, while larger-sized pieces saturated with water remain immune from attack.

The lower limit of moisture content that will permit fungal growth and decay is of much greater practical importance, as it is so often the crucial factor that determines whether or not decay will become established in a building or a boat.

Fungal spores do not germinate readily on wood which is below the fibre saturation point, that is to say below about 27 or 28 per cent, but timber cannot be regarded as completely immune from attack until it has dried down to a moisture content of 20--22 per cent. It must be realized that the moisture content of a large piece of wood is seldom uniform throughout, and though its average may be, say 25 per cent, it is likely that the deeper seated portions may be very much wetter. If the spores can find their way to this wetter area, through splits for instance, they can germinate and set up internal decay. Once a fungus of the dry-rot type is established in a moist pocket it can spread outwards into dryer wood taking its moisture along with it. (See Chapter 10.)

As a result of the chemical decomposition of wood by

fungi a certain amount of moisture is produced from the hydrogen and oxygen present in the cellulose molecules, so that, by decomposing the wood substance, the fungus can actually raise the moisture content of a piece of wood, thereby accelerating the process of decomposition. Partially decayed wood absorbs water much more readily than does sound, and retains it for longer, so that, once decay is established, the wood tends to remain in a wet condition for a longer time than does sound wood.

In a living tree the moisture content of the sapwood is generally too high to permit fungal growth, and it is only when the dead and dryer heartwood is exposed to infection that fungi are likely to gain entrance to the trunk.

When a log is sawn up into planks it is important to dry off their surface quickly before fungal growth can become established. Once there is a dry skin on the surface of the boards there is little risk of their becoming infected.

(4) *Oxygen Requirements.* There are a few organisms, mostly bacteria such as those that spoil canned foodstuffs, that can grow in the complete absence of oxygen, but most fungi demand at least some air for their growth, and many species die quite quickly if they are deprived of it. They need oxygen just as animals do, for their respiration i.e. for the oxidation of the sugars which they use for their growth and for their supply of energy. As a result of their respiration, fungi, like animals, produce carbon dioxide gas (CO_2), and if there is no interchange of air around the growing hyphæ CO_2 will accumulate and check their growth, and eventually the fungus will die as a result of suffocation. It is for this reason that wood-rotting fungi cannot grow on wood that is waterlogged.

Many examples could be quoted of the durability of timber under water; for instance, how the Elm piles below the foundations of old Waterloo Bridge were found to be quite sound after having been embedded in Thames mud for 130 years. This wood had acquired a pleasing grey colour and, after seasoning, some of it was eventually made into furniture! It is true that slow changes do take place over hundreds of years in wood submerged under water or buried in a bog, but these changes are of a different nature from those which occur in ordinary fungal decay, and may possibly be due in part to bacterial action. Bog Oak, which may have lain for thousands of years in a peat bog, is often very hard owing to the infiltration of minerals, and it is much prized for inlaying. I have also seen very beautiful Black Oak taken from the timbers of a Spanish galleon, sunk at Tobermory at the time of the Armada, which had been made into a cigarette case.

Practical use is made of the resistance to decay of wood submerged under water, and, while awaiting conversion, logs are often stored in specially constructed ponds. So long as they are kept submerged they remain free from decay and from insect attack, and do not develop end splits. This is often the best method for the protection of logs of perishable timber such as Birch and Aspen. It is a particularly suitable method of storing peeler logs destined for manufacture into veneer for plywood or matches, as any drying out of such logs is most undesirable.

If water is thoroughly aerated, as in a water-cooling tower where it tumbles down over a series of slats against a rising stream of air, it may contain sufficient dissolved oxygen to permit fungi to grow in the slats. The fungi which occur under these circumstances are cellulose destroying micro-fungi, and not the ordinary wood-rotting Basidiomycetes.

(5) *Temperature.* Fungi, like ordinary green plants, grow faster in warm weather than in cold. One goes to look for mushrooms when the weather is warm and the ground is moist. When the temperature is at freezing point, or only a few degrees

above it, fungi can make little or no growth, though the mycelium is not killed even by temperatures well below freezing point. So, though the fructifications of the more fleshy species may be shrivelled by frost, the most severe winter weather will not kill fungal mycelium inside a tree or in the soil.

For each species of fungus there is an *optimum* temperature at which growth is most rapid, and a *maximum* temperature above which growth cannot take place. For most fungi that grow in this country the optimum temperature lies between 80° and 90°F; while the maximum may be as high as 110°F,

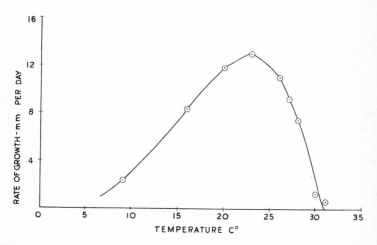

Fig. 4. Relation between temperature and rate of growth of *Fomes annosus* on malt agar.

but more often it lies between 95 and 100°F. In Fig. 4, the relation between the rate of growth and the temperature is shown graphically. It will be noted that there is a steady rise in the rate of growth with increasing temperatures up to the optimum, and above this a steeper falling off. Very roughly it can be said that fungi grow twice as fast for every 20°F rise in temperature, e.g. fungi will grow twice as fast at 70°F as they do at 50°F, and four times as fast at 90°F as at 50°F. The practical result of this is that wood decays more rapidly in the summer than it does in the winter, and very much more rapidly in the tropics than it does in temperate countries. For this reason it is unwise to leave logs of perishable species lying on the ground for any length of time during the warmer months of the year; while in the tropics it is always necessary to bring such logs out of the jungle without any delay at all.

Any fungus will be killed by prolonged exposure to temperatures above the maximum for growth, but it is difficult to define the thermal death point exactly, as this is, in fact, a function of both temperature and time. That is to say, a long exposure to a temperature only a little above the maximum will kill fungi just as surely as a shorter exposure to a somewhat higher temperature. For instance, in one experiment it was found that it required nine hours' exposure at 140°F to kill a culture of *Lentinus lepideus*, while at 150°F only one hour was needed. The lethal effects of high temperatures are also influenced by the condition of the fungus and the amount of moisture present. If the fungus is in active growth in a humid atmosphere it will be killed more easily than if it is in a dormant state in a dry condition. When infected timber is being sterilized by heat the humidity should be kept as high as possible. Provided the atmosphere around the wood is more or less saturated, the following times and temperatures have been found to sterilize effectively wood infected with the most heat-resistant species of wood-rotting fungi:

75 minutes at 150°F.
30 minutes at 180°F.
10 minutes at 200°F.
5 minutes at 212°F.

The heat must, of course, be applied for sufficiently long to allow it to permeate throughout the thickness of the pieces undergoing the treatment, and the time needed for the heat to penetrate must be added to the exposure periods quoted above.

Other Factors Influencing Growth of Fungi

We have so far been considering the essentials for fungal growth. Among the other influences that affect the development of fungi, one of the most important is light. In general, light has a retarding influence in fungal growth, while exposure to intense light, such as bright sunlight, can actually kill the mycelium of some species. But though most fungi grow more vigorously in the dark than in the light, many species cannot fructify normally in total darkness. *Lentinus lepideus*, for instance, which in the light produces a typical toadstool type of fruit body, in complete darkness forms only branched stalks that look almost like a branch of seaweed. (See Fig. 49.) Many fungi produce queer, abnormal fruit bodies on the pit props in mines, though even such a short exposure to light as a few minutes a week may be sufficient to stimulate the formation of a normal fruit body.

The effects of other types of radiation on fungi have also been studied, and it has been found that ultra-violet rays, which have a lethal effect on bacteria, can also kill exposed mycelium. In practice, however, these can seldom be used successfully for the sterilization of wood as infection is usually deep seated. X-rays appear to have little effect on fungi, though they may induce hereditary changes in spores. Dosages of X-rays that would be fatal to animals have been shown to have little effect on cultures of the Dry Rot Fungus.

The growth of fungi may also be affected by the degree of acidity or alkalinity of the substratum. Most kinds of wood have naturally a slightly acid reaction; and most fungi, indeed all the wood inhabiting species, flourish on materials which are slightly acid in reaction, and very few can tolerate alkaline conditions. Wood-rotting fungi generally produce appreciable amounts of organic acids as a result of their growth processes, and they tend thereby to increase the acidity of the wood in which they are growing. This process may intensify the corrosion of metal fittings in contact with moist timber. It has also been found that the treatment of wood with nitrogenous materials stimulates the growth of wood-rotting fungi; therefore contamination of wood by urine or manure is likely to render it more susceptible to decay. This effect of nitrogen in accelerating the decay of wood is made use of when it is wished to compost sawdust for use as a top dressing on the land.

EFFECTS OF DECAY ON WOOD

It is often important to be able to recognize incipient decay in wood, as this may have quite a serious effect on its strength and render it unfit for many purposes such as the manufacture of aircraft, ladders, sports goods and so on, where maximum strength is essential. We can classify the effects of decay of wood under two headings, chemical and physical. Let us consider them in that order as the nature of the physical changes depends on the type of chemical attack induced by the fungi.

Chemical Effects of Decay

Fungi obtain nourishment by absorbing it through the walls of their hyphæ. In order to do this they must first liquefy their food materials, and this is done by the secretion of enzymes by the hyphæ into the substances in which they are growing. (These enzymes are also known as ferments or "digestive juices".) Cellulose, which is the main constituent of wood substance, is, as already explained, built up in the tree by polymerization of glucose units. By means of enzymes a fungus can hydrolize the cellulose back into glucose which it can absorb. All wood-rotting fungi can break down cellulose

48

in this way. Those that attack only the cellulose and associated polysaccharides cause the wood to darken in colour, to shrink, and to crack up into brick shaped pieces which crumble easily into a brown powder. These are referred to as "brown rots". (See Fig. 5A.) There are other fungi (mostly those that grow in hardwoods) that can, in addition to their attack on the cellulose, break down the lignin by means of oxidizing enzymes. These fungi cause the wood to become paler in colour, and may eventually reduce it to a fibrous whitish mass; but they do not cause cross-cracking. Rots of this kind are commonly known as "white rots". It must be noted that in the first stage of a white rot there is often a dark discoloration which later may appear as a dark margin to the paler coloured wood. Sometimes white rot is localized and appear as small lens-shaped holes filled with a white lint-like material. (See Fig. 5B.)

Fig. 5. Types of fungal decay. C.C.R.
A. Brown crumbling rot in a softwood.

The term "soft rot" has been applied to a form of decay which is caused by cellulose-destroying micro-fungi. It is often superficial in nature, and is more commonly found in hardwoods than in coniferous softwoods. Wood decomposed by soft rot is of a dull, darkish colour, and has a cheesy consistency

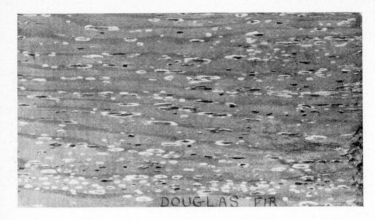

Fig. 5.B. White pocket rot in imported Douglas Fir, caused by *Trametes pini*.

when moist, and breaks with a short brash fracture. If it has been exposed to leaching and erosion by water the surface may, on drying, crack up into small brick-shaped pieces.

Fig. 5.C. White rot in Beech showing dark zone indicative of decay (dote).

The fungi that grow in wood synthesize various chemical compounds, as already mentioned. Some of them, particularly the brown rots, produce appreciable quantities of organic acids. A few produce sweet-smelling, aromatic substances which give a characteristic odour to the decayed wood. *Lentinus lepideus*, which is the principal cause of decay in poorly creosoted sleepers and poles, produces a smell reminiscent of balsam.

Physical Effects of Decay

Loss in Density. As decay progresses in a piece of wood the latter becomes gradually lighter in weight, owing to the destruction of the wood substance by the fungus, which gives off carbon dioxide and water during its respiration. Wood in an advanced stage of decay may be extremely light, though if the rot is a white one it may still retain its outward form. When carrying out laboratory experiments with wood-rotting fungi measurement of this loss in weight (expressed as a percentage of the original dry weight) is a useful method of assessing the extent to which decay has progressed.

Since brown rots cannot break down the lignin, they cannot decompose the whole of the wood, and the maximum loss of weight which they can cause is about 70 per cent. White rots, on the other hand, can totally destroy the wood. Abnormal lightness in a piece of wood is sometimes taken by inspectors to indicate the presence of decay, but though this often is the case, the test is unreliable, as samples of wood can often be found having a specific gravity far below the average for the species and yet being quite free from decay. However, from a practical point of view the test is useful because samples which are below the average density are always weaker than wood of normal weight, and therefore rejection on this ground alone may be justified.

Loss in Strength. While everyone knows that really rotten wood has little or no strength, it is not always realized what a

51

serious effect incipient decay may have on wood that is still hard and firm to the touch. Even slight decay can greatly reduce the toughness (shock resistance) of wood, and even before any appreciable loss in weight has occurred the toughness may have fallen off by half, and the wood will break off short with a carroty, brash fracture, instead of a splintery fracture.

Fungi that cause brown rots bring about a more rapid drop in most strength properties than do those which cause white rots, though both types soon reduce the toughness of any piece of wood they attack.

Increase in Permeability. Decayed wood absorbs liquid, and becomes waterlogged much more readily than does sound wood; presumably the tiny holes made by the fungal hyphæ in the cell walls allow the air to escape and so facilitate the entry of water. It is therefore particularly important that wood used for floats (Balsa for example) should be quite free from decay.

Preservatives penetrate more easily into partially decayed wood than into sound wood. It has been found, for instance, that slight incipient decay in spruce poles permits creosote to penetrate more readily.

Change in Colour. Incipient decay usually results in some abnormal coloration of the wood. In softwoods the first indication of decay is often the appearance of brown streaks or blotches, and sometimes purplish streaks are present. In hardwoods, such as beech or ash, whitish or pale-coloured spots or blotches are often the first sign of dote. Narrow, sharply defined dark lines bounding, or passing through, bleached areas are nearly always an indication of decay. These "zone lines" are most common in hardwoods, such as beech or birch, and the appearance of wood affected with these lines is sometimes quite decorative. (See Fig. 5.)

It is, of course, necessary to be familiar with the appearance of the normal sound wood of any species before deciding if the presence of coloured streaks is an indication of unsoundness. In many softwoods long streaks of a darker colour may occur which are due to a heavy deposit of resin. These resin streaks tend to be longer and more uniform in width than are the markings due to dote. Some woods naturally have lines or zones of varying colour. Parana Pine, for example, often shows a zone of vivid red colour at the junction of the sap and the heartwood.

Loss in Calorific Value. As the density of wood falls through the action of decay, so also does its calorific value as fuel. For practical purposes this means that the heating value of decayed wood is less than that of sound wood even though the volume of the wood remains almost the same. Logs destined for firewood should, therefore, be stacked openly so that they will dry out quickly without decaying and thus losing their calorific value.

Increase in Flammability. Decayed wood ignites more readily than sound and it tends to smoulder If there are any decayed areas in a door or post from which paint is being removed with a blowlamp these will quite likely begin to smoulder. It is, therefore, unwise to sterilize the surface of decayed beams with a blowlamp, as the smouldering wood may not be noticed, and some hours later, when the workmen have left the building, may burst into flames. Incidentally, it may be mentioned here that charring wood does *not* give it any adequate protection against subsequent infection although the belief that it does is persistent.

Luminescence. One or two fungi that occur in this country can cause wood in which they are growing to become luminescent and to glow in darkness with a pale bluish light. Francis Bacon studied "the wood that shineth in the dark", and rightly associated the production of light with putrefaction. The Honey Fungus, *Armillaria mellea*, which forms black strands that

53

E

penetrate under the bark of trees at ground level, is able, when in active growth, to render the wood luminous in this way. During the war, when firewatchers were wandering around at night on duty in timber yards, many inquiries were received as to the cause of this luminosity. Some people suspected it was due to contamination of the timber with phosphorus from enemy bombs! The luminescence of the infected wood persists, as Bacon noted, only for as long as the wood is moist and the fungus still in active growth. Use has sometimes been made of such luminous wood to mark out paths in a forest, and soldiers in the First World War sometimes found it useful to prevent collisions in the trenches.

Change in Smell. Wood that is decayed loses the usual "woody" smell, which is fresh and resinous, and it may, especially when damp, have a distinctly mushroomy odour. The smell of true dry rot is very distinctive and, once it has been smelt, is readily recognized again. As already mentioned, some wood-rotting fungi produce characteristic aromatic or sweet smells.

Increased Liability to Insect Attack. Wood that has been softened by decay is much more readily attacked by certain wood-boring insects, such as the Death-Watch Beetle, than is sound wood. (See page 94.) There are, in fact, many insects that can live only in wood that is partially decayed.

Microscopic Effects of Decay

When a thin section of a piece of decayed wood is examined under the microscope it is difficult to observe the hyphæ of the fungus, and their effect on the cell walls of the wood, unless the section is treated with appropriate dyes, and mounted on a glass slide, in a clearing fluid under a cover slip.

To obtain sufficiently thin sections of any size for observation by transmitted light it is best to use a special strongly constructed microtome in which a heavy knife makes a sliding cut through the specimen at an angle to the grain. These sliding microtomes, which in the past have mostly been made by firms abroad, such as Reichert, have a special device by which the block is automatically raised a definite amount after each cut, so that each section will be of the same thickness. The most suitable thickness varies somewhat according to the type of wood. Twenty to thirty microns is usually a convenient thickness with which to work. As the cost of these microtomes may amount to £150 they are not available in every botanical laboratory.

However, it is possible to obtain small hand sections by using a strong razor, especially if the blocks from which they are to be taken have undergone some preliminary softening. After a little practice it should be possible to cut these sections sufficiently thin to show the necessary details, at least in some parts. Decayed wood and fresh green wood of the softer kinds can often be sectioned (especially parallel to the grain) without any preliminary softening, though it is always advisable to soak the blocks before attempting to section them; and, in any case, the surface of the blocks, and the knife, must be kept wet. The denser kinds of wood, even when they are partially decayed, may require softening, and the simplest way to do this is to boil the blocks (which should measure about 1/2 in. × 1/4 in.) gently in water until they sink. Fragile material can be waterlogged by submersion in a vessel from which the air has been drawn by means of a vacuum pump. Really hard woods can be softened by boiling in a mixture of one part of glacial acetic acid and two parts of hydrogen peroxide (" 20 volumes " strength) in a reflux condenser. After the sections have been cut from the block they must be kept in water until they are stained.

For the detection of fungal hyphæ in wood the following treatment has been found to give consistently satisfactory results:

(1) Place the section (usually a longitudinal one) on a glass slide. Cover with 1 per cent aqueous safranin solution for one minute, or rather less.

(2) Wash with distilled water.

(3) Stain in picro-aniline blue (prepared by mixing one part of a saturated solution of aniline blue in water with four parts picric acid), and warm over a small flame until the fluid is almost at boiling point.

(4) Wash thoroughly with distilled water.

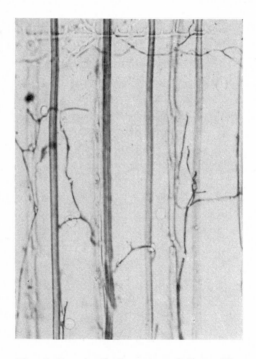

Fig. 6. Longitudinal section of Scots Pine infected with *Poria monticola* showing hyphæ of the fungus and the bore holes they have made in the cell walls. C.C.R.

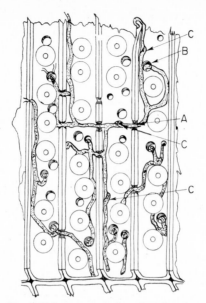

Fig. 7. Diagrammatic drawing showing
hyphæ of wood-rotting fungus in
tracheids of a softwood. Highly magnified. Note bore holes seen in section
at A and in plan at B and clamp connections on the hyphæ at C.

(5) Wash in several changes of 97 per cent alcohol, and
finally with absolute alcohol.

(6) Clear the section in clove oil, wash in cedarwood oil
or xylol, and mount in Canada balsam.

Sections treated in this way should show the lignified cells
of the wood stained red and the fungal hyphæ dark blue. In
severely decayed wood the cell walls may have a purplish tinge,
and not stain a clear red colour.

When a section of decayed wood is examined under the
microscope fungal hyphæ can usually be seen in all the elements

of the wood. To observe details of their structure it is necessary to use a fairly high magnification, such as that provided by 1/6 in. objective used with × 10 eyepiece. The number of hyphæ seen depends on the species of fungus present and the stage of decay the wood has reached. Sometimes the vessels may be almost filled with a mass of hyphæ, while in other samples only a few hyphæ will be seen. The hyphæ of almost all wood-rotting fungi can penetrate the cell walls by boring through them. (See Fig. 7.) The hyphæ of Basidiomycetes penetrate the walls at right angles to the long axis of the cells, whereas those of the micro-fungi that cause soft rot tunnel within the thickness of the wall, seeking out the least lignified middle layers of the

Fig. 8. Microscopic appearance of soft rot. C.C.R. A. Transverse section showing cross-section of hyphal tunnels in the secondary cell walls.

cell wall. (See Fig. 8.) Some fungi enlarge the holes after they have penetrated the wall and the hyphæ can then be seen passing through a hole of greater diameter than itself. (See Fig. 6.) Occasionally in severely decayed wood few hyphæ are left and only the bore holes remain as evidence of their earlier presence. Fungi that cause white rot usually cause a

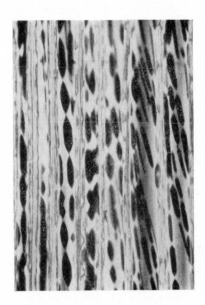

Fig. 8. B. Longitudinal section showing tunnels and prism-shaped cavities in the thickness of the cell walls.

general thinning of the cell walls in addition to the formation of bore holes.

Most wood-rotting fungi belonging to the *Basidiomycetes* bear on their hyphæ buckle-like structures known as clamp connections. (See Figs. 6,7.) If hyphæ bearing these structures are seen in the wood it is safe to conclude that some wood-rotting fungus is present. On the other hand the absence of clamp connections is no proof that the hyphæ belong to a non-decaying fungus. It must be explained at this point that many fungi, such as the common green moulds, can grow in and through wood without appreciably affecting it. These fungi, which derive their nourishment from extraneous food materials in the wood, such as sugars and starch, may cause unpleasant discolorations if their hyphæ are dark-hued, but are without appreciable effect on the strength of the timber.

It is only when the attack is in an early stage, or the symptoms are indefinite or unusual, that it is necessary to resort to microscopic examination to prove the absence or presence of suspected decay. Such examination is particularly useful when dealing with an unfamiliar timber or defect. It is only after considerable experience in the microscopic examination of wood sections that one can determine with any degree of certainty the nature and degree of any fungal infection from the appearance of the hyphæ in the wood; and it is practically impossible to decide by this method whether the hyphæ were alive at the time the section was cut.

THE CULTURING OF FUNGI

It is often important to know whether the fungus that has been responsible for decay in a piece of wood is still alive and capable of doing further damage. Of course, if fresh growths of mycelium, or fruit bodies, have been found on the suspected timber, those in themselves provide evidence of the fungus's vitality. But far more often than not no surface growths are present, and the only way to discover whether the fungus is still alive is to try to make it grow. The simplest way of doing this is to soak a piece of the wood (say six inches long) for a few hours until its weight has increased by about half, and then to keep it in a covered glass jar for a few weeks, in a moderately warm place. If the fungus in the wood is still alive it will, sooner or later, revive and form growths on the surface of the wood. Some fungi, when treated in this way, quite readily form fructifications and thereby reveal their identity; but others form only rather featureless growths which tell nothing about the fungus except that it is alive.

It has been discovered that fungi will form characteristic growths from which the species can be recognized if they can be isolated in pure culture on nutrient jelly. For this the same kind of technique is employed that bacteriologists use for the identification of the pathogenic bacteria which they isolate from human beings or animals suffering from infectious diseases. In laboratories devoted to the study of timber decay collections of standard cultures have been built up. These cultures are prepared from normal fructifications of a wide range of timber-rotting fungi, so that cultures of all the commoner species are now available for comparison with unidentified fungi isolated from samples sent in for diagnosis. At the Forest Products Research Laboratory at Princes Risborough some 400 species of wood-inhabiting fungi are maintained in culture, and are available for reference purposes.

The preparation of pure culture is difficult without the resources of a properly equipped mycological laboratory. The nutrient media used must always be sterilized, and the operations involved require the use of aseptic methods of transfer. The main difficulty encountered in this work is to avoid contamination of the cultures with quick-growing moulds. These, like weeds in a garden, will soon swamp the growth of the less rapidly growing wood-rotting fungi. Anyone who wishes to undertake pure culture work would be well advised to seek advice from a qualified mycologist or bacteriologist.

CHAPTER 5

Discolorations, Stains and Blemishes

In the range of tones characteristic of any particular timber there is usually a certain amount of natural variation. Some timbers, like Walnut and Indian Silver Grey Wood, have irregular dark markings in their heartwood that are quite normal and characteristic of the species. Others, such as Ash, which are usually pale in colour, occasionally possess a dark heartwood which is in no way associated with incipient decay. Then again many softwoods can be found on occasion to contain unusually plentiful deposits of resin which may give rise to dark-coloured streaks or definite resin pockets. It is therefore necessary to be familiar with the range of natural variation in colour within a species of timber before deciding whether any queer coloration is in fact abnormal and due to extraneous causes.

Discoloration or staining in timber can usually be attributed to one of the following causes:

(1) Oxidization of substances in the wood.

(2) Incipient decay.

(3) Growth on, or through, the wood of sap-staining and other fungi.

(4) Contact with chemical substances.

(5) Overheating—leading finally to charring.

(6) Weathering.

(1) OXIDIZATION STAINS

Some woods contain substances which, if the surface of the wood remains in a moist condition for any length of time, become oxidized by contact with the air. This staining is similar in origin to the browning that many fruits (the apple, for instance) show when they are cut and exposed to the air. It is due to the presence in the wood of an oxidizing enzyme which, in the presence of oxygen, acts on substances already in the wood to form coloured compounds. Some of these stains, such as the pale pink of freshly felled Ash, or the reddish-orange colour of newly cut Alder, soon fade away. Others, however, like the grey stain that appears in Sycamore that has been left

TABLE 3. Distinguishing Features of Decay and Sap-Stain

Incipient Decay	Sap-stain and Mould Staining
Not always confined to sapwood, though often more severe in sapwood.	Usually confined to sapwood. Sometimes quite superficial.
In form of blotches or streaks.	Often generally distributed but especially in the rays. Stained areas generally wedge-shaped when seen on end grain.
Colour in softwoods usually dark brown, sometimes purplish. In hardwoods, either whitish or dark-brown spots or streaks.	Colour blue-grey, green or blackish, occasionally pink, yellow, or orange.
Narrow black zone lines may be present, especially in hardwoods.	Sharply defined zone lines never present.
Fibres weakened, breaking off short when tested with a knife.	No appreciable weakening of the fibres.

to lie in the log, or the greyish-black stain in Persimmon, persist and render the wood unfit for certain purposes. For instance, when Sycamore is to be used for pastry-boards, or Persimmon for golf-club heads, a clean bright appearance is essential. Quick conversion of the logs after felling and rapid drying of the sawn timber will do much to reduce the risk of this type of staining. In the case of Persimmon a short steaming treatment, which destroys the enzymes in the wood, has been found to prevent this stain from developing.

(2) INCIPIENT DECAY

The changes in colour induced by incipient decay have already been described. Generally they involve either a bleaching effect (in hardwoods) or the development of dark brown patches or streaks. More rarely incipient decay in softwoods is accompanied by purplish streaks. The distinguishing features between incipient decay and sap-stain are, for convenience, given in Table 3.

(3) SAP-STAINING FUNGI

Many kinds of fungi grow on damp timber besides those which are capable of destroying its substance and bringing about actual decay. Some of these have little or no visible effect on the wood or, at most, produce a mere bloom on the surface. However this superficial growth of green, or blackish, mould can be troublesome at times—for instance if it occurs on box-boards used for the manufacture of cases for foodstuffs or soap, where a clean, sanitary appearance is essential. Even so they can usually be removed quite easily either by brushing or planing the surface.

More serious are the moulds that cause the deep seated dark staining commonly known as sap-stain. Since the fungi responsible for this derive their nourishment from the reserve food materials (starches and sugars) stored in the living cells, they normally develop only in sapwood, or, where there is no clearly defined sapwood and heartwood, in the outer layers of the trunk where these materials are stored. (See Fig. 9.) If a section of stained sapwood is examined under the microscope

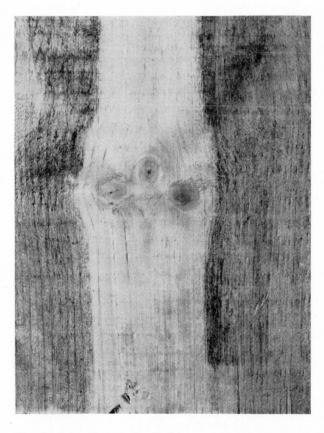

Fig. 9. Baltic Redwood with blue stain in the sapwood.
C.C.R.

it will be seen that the dark colour of the wood is due to the presence in the cells of large numbers of dark brown hyphæ of the sap-stain fungus. The hyphæ of these fungi often pass from one cell to another through the natural openings (pits) in the cell walls. Some of them, however, are capable of penetrating the actual cell walls, through which they make exceedingly fine bore holes very much smaller than the normal diameter of the hyphæ themselves, so that the latter are much constricted during the passage. (See Fig. 10.) Hyphæ of the staining fungi never enlarge the bore holes after they have passed through, as do some of the rotting fungi.

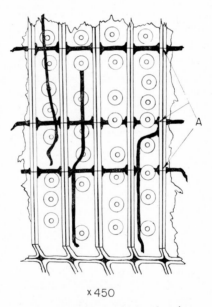

x 450

Fig. 10. Diagrammatic drawing showing hyphæ of sap stain fungi in the tracheids of softwood. Note exceedingly fine penetrations at A. Highly magnified.

Sap-stain often has a definite bluish tinge, and it is then commonly referred to as "blue-stain"; but no blue pigment is actually secreted by the fungi, and the cell walls in such stained wood can be seen to have retained their normal pale colour. The bluish tinge has been explained as an optical phenomenon similar to that which sometimes makes smoke appear blue though it is actually composed of black particles. The numerous dark coloured hyphæ seen through the translucent cell walls of the wood give this blue, or blue-grey effect.

Since the reserve food materials on which sap-stain fungi feed are stored mainly in the rays, it is in these that the hyphæ of such fungi tend to grow most vigorously. A cross-section of a stained log usually shows wedge-shaped areas of stain, and even with the naked eye one can see how the stain runs in along the rays.

There are a number of different species of wood-inhabiting fungi which possess dark coloured hyphæ and are capable of causing staining. On softwoods the commonest are species of *Ceratostocystis*. These belong to a genus of *Ascomycetes* in which the fructification consists of a small, round, blackish perithecium about the size of a pin's head. From the top of this grows a long thin neck, up to a $1/_4$ in. or so in length, which to the naked eye looks like a stout piece of horsehair. (See Fig. 11.) The ascopores, which are discharged from the asci inside the perithecium, are forced up the neck and ooze as a slime out of the opening at the tip. The spores are sticky and become distributed in splashing drops of rainwater, or by insects and mites.

× 100

Fig. 11. Fruiting body (perithecium) of sap-stain fungus *Ceratostocystis* sp.

In tropical hardwoods the most common cause of staining is a species of *Diplodia*. This fungus sometimes forms a thick waft of blackish mycelium on the surface of the stained wood if it is kept for any length of time in a humid atmosphere. It produces its spores inside small, round, black, spherical bodies known as *pycnidia*.

Many of the staining fungi possess more than one type of spore, and in consequence are capable of very rapid reproduction. These spores, like those of the wood-rotting fungi, germinate only if sufficient moisture is present. Sap-stain fungi can grow very rapidly under favourable conditions, and in warm weather it is possible for sapwood to become stained throughout in a matter of weeks. Under tropical conditions it may be almost impossible to get logs of susceptible species out of the jungle before staining becomes established. (See Chapter 9.) The surface of freshly sawn lumber can soon become infected with staining fungi in warm weather if it does not dry off quickly; and stain is also very liable to develop if planks are left for more than a few days in solid piles.

Though most of the stains caused by sap-staining fungi are bluish or grey in colour, other tints can be produced by moulds. Oak, and a few other hardwoods, sometimes show quite a bright yellow colour in the sapwood; and Oak stained in this way has been called "golden oak", although the stained material scarcely merits such a title! The mould responsible can grow at surprisingly high temperatures (up to 110°F) and this is sometimes the cause of trouble during the early stages of the kiln drying of Oak and other dense timbers that cannot be exposed to higher temperatures without risk of damage by splitting.

Orange-pink stains are sometimes caused by species of *Penicillium*, but this discoloration is often quite superficial. Purplish stains are often caused by *Fusarium* spp.

Effect of Sap-stain on Properties of Wood

Numerous tests have been carried out to find whether sap-stain reduces the mechanical strength of wood. The general conclusion has been that it has no significant effect on the bending or compressive strength, and does not appreciably reduce the hardness of wood. It does, however, slightly reduce the toughness (shock resistance), and heavily stained wood should not therefore be used in the construction of aircraft, or sports goods where maximum toughness is desirable. For most constructional purposes sap-stained wood can be used with perfect safety, and there is no objection to using it in buildings for roofing and carcassing. Once the timber is seasoned the stain will not develop further; and, though it has been suggested that blue-stained wood is more liable than bright wood to become attacked by dry rot, the difference in decay resistance has in fact been shown to be so slight as to have no practical significance. But it must also be remembered that the presence of blue stain in softwood is a sure indication that sapwood is present, and this in itself is less resistant to decay than is heartwood. If sapwood is present, whether stained or bright, it should receive preservative treatment if there is any risk of the timber becoming damp in use.

If paint is applied to heavily-stained sapwood in which there is still a certain amount of moisture the mould may grow through the paint film and discolour that also. This can be prevented by ensuring that the wood is thoroughly seasoned before it is painted, and by applying an antiseptic to the wood before applying the paint.

Occurrence of Sap-stain

Timbers vary greatly in their liability to sap-stain. Of the softwoods, Pine is much more susceptible than Larch, Spruce or Douglas Fir, though in all of these the sapwood will stain if there is delay in converting the logs, or if, owing to faulty

69

F

piling or unfavourable weather, the seasoning of the freshly sawn green timber is delayed. Though blue stain is occasionally found in samples of Ash and Aspen-Poplar, none of the European hardwoods is particularly prone to stain; but many of the light-coloured tropical varieties, such as Obeche, Limba, Celtis, and Ramin, are highly susceptible, and special precautions must be taken if they are to be obtained in a clean condition. (See Chapter 9.) Superficial growths of mould can occur on almost any kind of wood if it is kept for long enough in a damp atmosphere, but it is most troublesome on the sapwood of timbers, such as Obeche, that contain a large amount of starch.

Stain in tropical hardwoods is very often associated with attack by Pinhole Borers (See page 85), and can be controlled only if these insects are prevented from infecting the logs.

Fungi that cause sap-stain, like those that cause dry rot, require a certain amount of air for their development, and are unable to penetrate into wood that is saturated with water. The moisture content of normal healthy sapwood is too high for their growth, and so it is rare to find sap-stain in standing trees unless large areas of bark have been damaged, thus allowing the underlying sapwood to dry out. In trees weakened by drought sap-stain fungi can be introduced by bark beetles.

Economic Significance of Sap-stain

While it is true that sap-stain has no appreciable effect on the strength or working properties of wood for most purposes, its presence may greatly reduce the commercial value of timber, particularly in those kinds in which a bright clean appearance is demanded. When it occurs in timbers that are used in their natural state for decorative purposes, such as shop fittings, furniture, etc., it may render the wood almost unsaleable. Manufacturers of matches are very particular about the colour of the wood which they use for making match splints; and packing-case makers also have a strong preference for clean timber as many of their customers demand clean and attractive-looking boxes in which to pack their products. Even in ordinary building softwoods the presence of stain is undesirable as there is a strong prejudice against using "blue wood". Though, for reasons already given, this prejudice often has no basis in fact, nevertheless a better price will usually be paid for clean timber than for blue, or mouldy, material. A wise timber producer will therefore take every precaution to prevent his timber from becoming stained during seasoning.

Prevention of Sap-stain

(a) *Logs.* In Northern Europe, where trees are usually felled and removed from the woods during the winter, staining of the logs is only troublesome when large stocks of logs have to be kept in storage for an unduly long time. The best way to protect logs from deterioration of all kinds is to store them under water, or to keep them soaking wet by means of an overhead spray. In the tropics special precautions may have to be taken to prevent staining of logs of susceptible species. (See page 160.)

(b) *Sawn Timber.* If the surface of freshly sawn timber can be dried off quickly enough there is little risk of the boards becoming stained, and, provided that drying conditions are reasonably good, proper piling of the sawn timber will ensure that most of it remains reasonably free from stain. If, however, the weather is humid and warm, susceptible timbers will become stained even if piled openly with plenty of ventilation. In West Africa and in the Gulf States of the U.S.A. atmospheric conditions may be favourable for the development of stain during most of the year. In Great Britain the months during which the risk of staining and mould are greatest are September, October and April.

Sap-stain can be entirely prevented, either by drying the

freshly sawn timber quickly in a drying kiln, or by dipping the boards in an antiseptic solution immediately after they have been sawn and then piling them openly to season in the air. There are very effective chemicals for the prevention of sap-stain fungi now on the market (See page 160) and sold under trade names such as Brunobrite, Crytogil, Permatox, Lignasan, Pulposan and Santobrite. It is very important that the boards should be dipped within twenty-four hours of coming from the saw. If the staining fungi and moulds succeed in penetrating even a fraction of an inch into the wood no chemical treatment will arrest their further spread, and surface treatment will merely result in a deceptively clean skin over a stained interior. Spraying of the boards with the solution is much less satisfactory than dipping them as it is difficult to ensure 100 per cent coverage of all the surfaces; also it is more wasteful of solution.

Stains due to Fungi other than Sap-stain Type

There are a number of stains caused by fungi which yet cannot be classed as sap-stains as the effect is not confined to the sapwood. Two well-known examples of these are "green wood" and "brown oak".

Green Wood. It is not uncommon to find in damp woods pieces of wood from such trees as Oak, Ash and Hazel which are stained almost throughout such a vivid, verdigris green that one could imagine that the wood had been soaked in a chemical dye or in green ink. This condition is caused by the growth through the wood of a fungus known as *Chlorosplenium æruginosum*, and sometimes its little, bright-green, leaf-like fructifications can be found on the surface of the stained wood. Though this fungus appears to grow usually on wood that has already been partially decayed by some other fungus, in the laboratory it can be induced to grow in, and to stain, pieces of quite sound timber. In fact, in 1911 a patent was filed by the late Professor T. Brooks to cover the use of this fungus for staining wood for decorative purposes. Naturally stained "green wood" has been used for the inlaid Tunbridge Wells ware, and it is in demand by artists who make pictures with veneers of naturally coloured woods. This natural dye is much more resistant to fading as a result of exposure to light than are most green chemical dyes. But though it is quite easy to find green-stained twigs, large pieces of green wood are rare. *Chlorosplenium* does not itself cause rot, but, as it so often grows on wood that has already been attacked, green wood is frequently so soft and friable that it is valueless for inlay work.

Brown Oak. It is not uncommon to find the heartwood of old Oak trees stained a rich, warm, brown colour, many shades darker than the normal heartwood. Sometimes this brown colour runs in bands, and usually there are darker-coloured stripes at the edges of the brown areas. It is very rare to find the whole of a trunk "brown". It has been shown that this colouring is due to a fungus known as the Beef-steak Fungus (*Fistulina hepatica*) which gains an entrance through large wounds in the trunk or branches, and slowly permeates the wood, spreading at first along and then across the grain, and causing a dark colouring matter to appear in the rays and wood parenchyma cells. It does not cause any appreciable decay until it has been acting on the wood for many years. The broad tongue-shaped fruit body (which only appears after the fungus has been growing in the tree for a long time) resembles raw steak in colour and texture, but not at all in flavour, even when grilled or fried. It is, however, considered a good esculent, but needs long cooking, being rather tough. The presence of these fruit bodies on the trunk of an Oak is a sure indication that at least a proportion of the heartwood will be "brown". Brown Oak, which is much prized for making into furniture or for panelling, is not quite as strong as normal wood, and should not, therefore, be used for constructional work or in boat building. There is, however, no risk of the Beef-steak Fungus continuing to grow and spread after the wood has been seasoned, and so Brown Oak can safely be used in furniture without fear of deterioration.

(4) CONTACT WITH CHEMICAL SUBSTANCES

Contact with iron is a very common cause of bluish-black staining in woods, such as Oak and Sweet Chestnut, that contain large amounts of tannin. The tannin reacts with the iron to form iron tannate, which is the basis of ordinary ink. If oak palings are fixed with ordinary iron wire or cut nails, disfiguring dark-blue streaks will soon appear under each nail, as the iron rust washes down with the rain and reacts with the tannin in the wood. This trouble can easily be avoided by using galvanized nails. Similarly, oak-faced plywood may show bluish stains if the glue used in its manufacture is contaminated with iron. The cause of an inky stain can easily be established by testing the wood for the presence of iron in the following way:

Moisten the surface of the wood with a drop of hydrochloric acid of approximately 15 to 20 per cent concentration (i.e. equal volumes of concentrated "Analar" acid and distilled water) from the end of a clean glass rod. From a second glass rod allow one drop of potassium ferrocyanide solution (approximately 2 oz $K_4Fe(CN)_6 3H_2O$ in 10 oz distilled water) to fall on the moistened area. An immediate blue colour indicates the presence of iron. If the condition of the wood surface makes it difficult to distinguish the colour *in situ* it may be transferred to clean filter paper by blotting the moist area of the wood.

Iron stains can be removed from wood by sponging the surface with a solution of oxalic acid containing approximately 1 oz of the acid crystals in 16 oz of either distilled water or methylated spirit. To effect a permanent removal of stain it is essential to wash the acid solution thoroughly from the wood either with distilled water or with clean methylated spirit. Both the acid solution and the washing fluid should be prepared and stored in glass or earthenware vessels, and nothing containing ferrous metals should be allowed to come in contact with these liquids or with the damp surface of the wood. Oxalic acid is poisonous and should be handled accordingly.

Contact with alkaline solutions such as ammonia or caustic soda causes darkening in many hardwoods, and is the basis for the process of fuming oak. Sometimes dark brown patches appear on the face of oak-faced plywood that has become damp. It has been found that these are caused by reaction of the oak veneer with ammonia produced by bacterial decomposition of the animal glue. Their formation can be prevented either by protecting the plywood from damp, or by using a synthetic resin glue that does not break down with the formation of ammonia under moist conditions.

Sometimes staining on the surface of plywood is the result of a dark-coloured glue being forced through the veneer during the process of manufacture.

(5) OVERHEATING

It is generally fairly obvious when dark brown staining has been due to the scorching of wood by heat. It is occasionally found in material dried in a kiln in which the temperature has not been properly controlled. It may also occur on the surface of wood cut with a saw that has been binding and developing excessive friction, or on pieces whose passage through a planer has been impeded by undue friction.

(6) WEATHERING

The colour of wood that is fully exposed to the weather in

this country generally fades, and the surface becomes, in clean air, a pleasing silvery-grey colour, due to the washing out of the coloured constituents of the wood by prolonged exposure to rain. In a dirty atmosphere the exposed surface may become a dark-grey colour; whereas in a dry climate with abundance of ultra-violet radiation the surface of untreated timber becomes darkened. Exposure of wood indoors to intense light may lead to fading of the surface layers, and furniture made of Mahogany and similar woods may change in colour if it is exposed for a long period to sunlight.

Few timbers can be left fully exposed to weather without suffering some breakdown of the surface and it is generally advisable to treat all surfaces of decorative woodwork that are left unpainted. Linseed oil, raw or boiled, is commonly used, but in dirty or damp atmospheres wood so treated often becomes discoloured. In recent years many attempts have been made to find really durable clear finishes which can be applied to decorative woodwork in the open. Unfortunately so far no product that lasts for more than two years without serious deterioration has been developed and regular re-treatment every two years is still necessary if a clear, bright surface must be maintained.

CHAPTER 6

Destruction of Wood by Insects 1.
Coleoptera, Hymenoptera and Lepidoptera

THE cost of replacing timber damaged by wood-boring insects amounts to a very large annual sum, even in temperate climates; while in tropical and sub-tropical countries these insects probably cause quite as much damage as do the wood-rotting fungi.

Insects form the largest group of living animals, probably exceeding in the number of species all the rest of the animal kingdom. They have immense powers of reproduction, and many species are represented by countless millions of individuals. They form one section of the phylum, or large group, of invertebrate animals known as the *Arthropoda*. In this group the body is composed of a series of segments placed one behind another, and possesses, as the name implies ("arthron" — a joint, and "pous", gen. "podos" — a foot), a series of jointed limbs or appendages. A characteristic feature is the possession of a hard external skin known as the *exoskeleton*, which not only serves as armour for the soft body within, but also provides attachment for the muscles, which in higher animals are fixed to the bones.

The body of the insect is divided into three distinct parts, each formed of a number of segments more or less fused together. The first of these is the head. The second is the thorax, and consists of three enlarged segments each of which bears a pair of legs on the underside, while the wings, when present, are borne on the upper, or dorsal, surface of two hindermost segments. The third part, the abdomen, consists of a varying number of segments, ten being the most usual: it carries no legs but in the females the ovipositor or egg-laying apparatus is sometimes prominent. Insects which live almost exclusively on land breathe by means of a system of air tubes which permeate the body. They have nothing, however, which corresponds to the lungs of higher animals, and the absence of any mechanism for circulating air through the body sets a limit to their size.

Most insects reproduce by means of very small eggs (See Fig. 12) from which hatch out the so-called larvae. Since the exoskeleton of insects is more or less rigid, growing insects have to shed their old skins by a process known as ecdysis and grow a new integument. Often the succeeding stages of the insects development, which are known as instars, differ only slightly one from another. In others the larvae differ completely both in appearance and structure from the adult insect, as for instance, in the case of butterflies and moths (*Lepidoptera*), and the change from the young grub to the adult in these groups is called "complete metamorphosis". In these insects there is a quiescent, or pupal, period between the larval and the adult stages, during which the creature ceases to feed and profound changes in its structure occur, often within the shelter of a hard casing or cocoon. In other insects, such as the cockroach, where the young bear a general resemblance to the adult, the metamorphosis is said to be "incomplete".

Insects are classified into a number of orders, which are based on:

(1) The structure of the mouth parts.
(2) The nature of the wings.
(3) The type of metamorphosis that occurs.

The nature of the mouth parts, whether they are designed for biting or for sucking, determines the way in which the insect will feed and the nature of the foodstuffs which it can use.

Nearly all the insects that cause serious damage to timber belong to one or other of the two orders:

> *Coleoptera*—the beetles.
> *Isoptera*—termites, or "white ants".

There are also a few caterpillars (*Lepidoptera*) which occur in trees, the Goat-Moth Caterpillar for instance; and several species of *Hymenoptera* (the order which includes ants, bees, wasps and ichneumon flies) which cause occasional damage.

COLEOPTERA

The beetles are probably the largest order of insects, and over 175,000 species have been described. The characteristic features of the group are:

(1) The possession of two pairs of wings, of which the forward pair are thickened and horny and are not used in flight; when closed they lie flat, covering the thin flying wings which fold under them.

(2) Mouth parts are designed for chewing.

(3) Body is usually rather stout, and the exoskeleton fairly thick and hard.

(4) Metamorphosis is complete. The egg hatches into larva (grub) which, when full grown, turns into a pupa from which eventually the adult beetle emerges.

The beetles that attack wood can conveniently be classified into four groups:

> Longhorn Beetles—*Cerambycidæ*.
> Pinhole Borers—*Scolytidæ* and *Platypodidæ*.
> Powder-post Beetles—*Bostrychidæ* and *Lyctidæ*.
> Furniture Beetles—*Anobiidæ*.

In addition to these (woodworms), wood-boring weevils belonging to the family *Curculionidæ* are often found in partially decayed wood, in which they cause secondary damage.

Longhorn Beetles—*Cerambycidæ*

The Longhorn Beetles constitute a large family, often easily recognized by the length of their antennæ ("horns"), which may be as long as the body of the insect itself. Many of the species are large and conspicuous, and some are brightly coloured. With one or two exceptions these beetles are inhabitants of fallen logs in the forest, acting as scavengers. Only a few cause serious damage to sawn timber, and fewer still to living, standing trees. When they do invade living trees it will usually be found that the tree attacked was already in an unhealthy or dying condition.

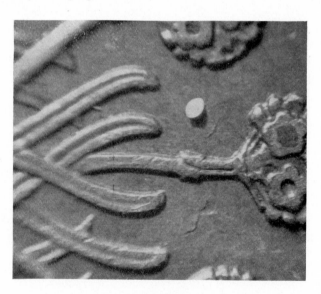

Fig. 12. Egg of a **Death**-Watch Beetle on a threepenny-piece.

The larvæ of all Longhorns are elongate, rather narrow grubs which taper slightly in width from head to tail. The body is slightly flattened dorsoventrally, and shows a number of rings or segments. These are whitish or pale cream in colour, but may show darker markings on the dorsal surface. The head is darker in colour, the jaws being almost black, and it is sometimes inconspicuous when partially withdrawn into the first segment of the body.

When taken from their tunnels they can move only very slowly and with difficulty. Their size, when full grown, depends on the species, and may be anything from half an inch to three inches or even more in length.

The first tunnels are usually made by the grubs between the bark and the wood which they eventually enter, and the holes which they bore there may be a quarter of an inch or more in diameter, and very often rather oval in section. The length of the larval life varies greatly according to conditions; it may be completed in one year, but often takes two or more. When the wood in which the larva is boring becomes dry the rate of development may be very slow indeed, and cases have been recorded in which beetles have emerged from furniture in which the larvæ must have lived for ten years or more. In one exceptional instance a piece of walnut furniture over twenty years old was found to contain living larvæ. It is only the larvæ that cause damage to timber; the beetles themselves do not bore. They are much commoner in hardwoods than in softwoods and generally the damage is confined to the sapwood, though in some woods, such as Ash, the larvæ can penetrate more deeply.

With the exception of the House Longhorn (see below) practically all Longhorn Beetles prefer to breed in fresh, unseasoned timber. The damage is, therefore, unlikely to spread in timber once it has been sawn up and seasoned, and there is little risk of it spreading to adjacent timber already stored

81

in the yard. In general one is much more likely to find Long-horn grubs in logs than in sawn timber.

Prevention of damage to felled timber by Longhorn Beetles largely depends on getting the logs out of the woods as soon as possible after they are felled. Removal of the bark from the logs immediately after felling will prevent beetles from laying their eggs and is an effective method of preventing infestation in many timbers. It must however be used with caution as some species of wood are liable to crack and split when the surface of the logs dries rapidly after removal of the bark.

House Longhorn—Hylotrupes bajulus

In contrast to most other Longhorns, which confine their attention to green logs, the House Longhorn is essentially a

Fig. 13. A. House Longhorn Beetle, *Hylotrupes bajulus*. Adult beetles, natural size, female below and male above.

pest of seasoned softwoods. During the last sixty years this pest has become widespread in North-Western Germany and in Denmark and has caused extensive damage to the roof timbers of large numbers of houses. (See Figs. 13, 14.) It has also become common in France and the Netherlands; and in the Cape

Fig. 13. B. Typical damage in softwood joist.

Peninsula, South Africa, it has caused such widespread damage that legislation to control its spread was introduced in 1948.

In England it had been found only sporadically until the 1930s when a widespread outbreak was discovered in certain districts in Surrey, where roof timbers in some hundred or

Fig. 13. C. Damage to joist showing bulges on the surface due to tunnelling and piles of bore dust on ceiling lath. C.C.R.

Fig. 14. Larva of House Longhorn Beetle, *Hylotrupes bajulus*, magnified × 2. C.C.R.

more houses were found to be severely damaged. It does not appear to have spread seriously beyond this area, which in the summer has the highest mean temperature in the country. As warm weather is known to favour the hatching of the eggs this may account for the limited distribution of the insect in England. Larvæ are sometimes found in imported packing-cases and orange boxes which can act as a source of infestation in new areas. It is therefore most important that its presence should be recognized without delay so that measures can be taken promptly to eradicate any infestations that may be found, before they have a chance to become widespread.

Only softwoods are attacked by this beetle and damage is usually confined to the sapwood. It has been shown that sapwood affected by blue stain is less suitable for the development of the larvæ than bright clean sapwood. Affected timbers may become so extensively tunnelled that they almost disintegrate, yet a thin skin of sound wood remains on the surface so that externally the wood looks quite sound, except for the flight holes made by the mature beetles as they emerge. These exit holes are oval and the longer diameter varies from $^1/_8$ in. to $^3/_8$ in. No bore dust is expelled from the tunnels and the attack is often difficult to detect if there are only a few exit holes. Sometimes the attack is discovered by someone hearing the noise made by the beetles when they bite their way out of the wood. Suspected timbers should be probed with a spike and, if Longhorn Beetle is found, expert advice should be sought, and immediate steps taken to get rid of the infestation by cutting away all the infected sapwood and throughly dressing the remaining timber with insecticide. The timber used for replacements should, whenever possible, be impregnated under pressure with a wood preservative.

Pinhole Borers—Scolytidæ and Platypodidæ

The so-called Pinhole Borers are small beetles, $^1/_8$ to $^1/_4$ in. in length, which infest freshly felled logs and, less commonly, standing trees, often boring deeply into the wood. They are much more common in timbers from tropical and sub-tropical countries than in those grown in Europe, though recently widespread attack has been reported on softwoods in Western Scotland. It should be noted that with Pinhole Borers it is the beetles themselves that tunnel in the wood and not the larvæ as with Longhorns. These insects derive little or no nourishment from the wood itself but feed on fungi introduced by the female beetle, which grow in the tunnels. These moulds, which have been called "ambrosia" (Pinhole Borers are sometimes called Ambrosia Beetles), usually stain the wood around the tunnels black, or very dark brown, and often this discoloration is more disfiguring than the holes themselves. (See Figs. 15, 16.)

Fig. 15. Pinhole Borer damage in tropical hardwoods showing dark staining around the holes.   C.C.R.

No bore dust is found in the tunnels, which usually run across the grain of the wood. Unless the pinholes are exceedingly numerous they have no effect on the strength of the wood, and so-called "sound-wormy" grades of many woods can safely be used for any purpose where an unblemished appearance is not essential. There is no risk of the beetles continuing to work and extend the damage in seasoned timber in use. Timber showing Pinhole-Borer damage should not therefore be discarded, but used in situations where the disfigurement is not important.

Nevertheless, there is considerable prejudice against timber showing any form of insect damage, and since the public cannot be expected always to distinguish between harmless Pinhole-Borer damage and attacks by more serious types of wood-borers, it behoves timber merchants to do all they can to reduce the amount of Pinhole-Borer damage. Logs of susceptible species

Fig. 16. Pinhole Borer damage in Oak. C.C.R.

can be protected against infestation by spraying them immediately after they have been felled with an effective insecticide solution. (See Chapter 8.) Early removal of logs from the forest and rapid conversion will do much to reduce the incidence of attack, and in Europe and the U.S.A. winter felling and removal of the logs from the forest before the insects are in flight will reduce the risk of infection of timbers such as Oak.

Powder-post Beetles—Bostrychidæ and Lyctidæ

The Powder-post Beetles, in contrast to the Longhorns, are pests of seasoned and partly seasoned timbers. They get

Fig. 17. Adult Platypodid Beetle. C.C.R.

their name from the fact that they reduce the wood to a fine flourlike powder.

The Bostrychids are most prevalent in warmer countries, and, in comparison with the Lyctid Beetles, are of minor importance in Europe. Both pests are of hardwood and confine their attacks to the sapwood. They derive their nourishment mainly from starch and reserve food materials stored in the parenchyma cells of the rays. The Bostrychids are of small or medium size, and most of them are dark brown in colour. The characteristic feature of the group is a hood-shaped roughened thorax armed with small spines which cover the head. The antennæ end in a three-jointed club. The larvæ are pale-coloured, wrinkled grubs, with brown jaws, and three pairs of four-jointed legs. Damage by Bostrychids can be prevented by the methods outlined below for the control of *Lyctus*.

Lyctus Beetles are some of the most troublesome pests of hardwoods, and cause serious loss both to timber merchants and to manufacturers of furniture, sports goods, tool handles, etc. There are a number of species, of which at least six occur in Great Britain. The adult beetles are small, narrow, dorso-ventrally flattened, and have a rather stream-lined appearance. (See Fig. 18.) They are dark brown in colour and about $1/5$ in. in length. The antennæ end in a two-jointed club. The larvæ are curved white grubs, about $1/4$ in. long when full grown, and the yellowish head has dark brown jaws. They can be distinguished from the Bostrychid larvæ by the presence of large spiracles, or breathing pores, on the eighth segment of the body.

The female beetle first tastes the wood to see if it is suitable for the development of her offspring—that is to say, whether it contains sufficient starch. She then inserts her long ovipositor (egg-laying tube) into the pores of the wood, wherein she deposits the long, thin eggs. Eggs are never laid on the suface of the wood, and it is very rare to find larvæ in woods in which

Fig. 18. Wood-boring beetles and their larvæ.
Top : Powder-post Beetle, *Lyctus* sp. Enlarged about 8 times.
Left : Death-Watch Beetle, *Xestobium rufo-villosum*. Enlarged
about 7 times. *Right :* Common Furniture Beetle, *Anobium punctatum*.
Enlarged about 10 times. (Larvæ also enlarged; see text for actual
sizes.)

the diameter of the pores (vessels) in less than that of the ovipositor. Small-pored woods, such as Beech, Horse Chestnut, and Pear are seldom, if ever, attacked by these beetles, which normally confine their attentions to such large-pored woods as Ash, Elm, Oak, Hickory and Walnut.

The larvæ at first tunnel in the direction of the vessels, but later they wander about in all directions, their tunnels often crossing each other, until the wood is reduced to powder. The larva forms its pupal chamber just under the surface of the wood, and the beetles emerge by cutting a hole, $^1/_{32}$ to $^1/_{16}$ in. in diameter, in this thin outer skin of sound wood. When emerging, the beetles will bore through heartwood or through a paint covering, and have been known to bore through wood covered with lead and even silver. The beetles emerge in the late spring or summer, and the whole life cycle normally takes a year, though it may be extended to two years if the wood contains only a little starch.

Infestation with *Lyctus* can be recognized if there are small piles of the fine wood dust on the surface of, or under, the suspected piece of furniture or timber. Sometimes, however, there is little sign of its presence until the adult beetles emerge, and wood that contains the eggs or young larvæ may appear quite sound, and thus be used unwittingly, its true condition only being discovered many months later.

Prevention of Lyctus damage depends in the first instance on reducing the risk of infestation by general hygiene in the timberyard. Stocks of susceptible timbers should be carefully inspected at least twice a year, and any infestations found should be dealt with immediately. New stock should be examined thoroughly for signs of attack before it is used or stored. Any infested material should be segregated at once, and the affected sapwood destroyed or, if the attack is in an early stage, sterilized. (See below.) General tidiness and the destruction or removal of offcuts and scraps of sapwood lying around the yard are of the utmost importance, as such material provides the breeding ground for new generations of insects. All piling sticks used for separating boards should be cut from heartwood, or from coniferous softwood which is immune to attack.

While the general use of insecticides for protection against *Lyctus* is not considered essential in this country, it may be desirable under special circumstances to give protection to stocks of susceptible timbers, when the risk of infestation is known to be high. If, sometime during the spring, all the sapwood can be covered with a spray containing 0.5 per cent BHC, or dieldrin, or 2 per cent D.D.T. it should remain immune from attack during the summer period when the beetles are emerging. When spraying stacks of timber it is necessary to use a sprayer with a long lance to ensure that the liquid really reaches all the sapwood. In Australia, dipping of veneers of susceptible woods in 4 per cent solution of boric acid at 140°F (60°C) has been found effective for protection of plywood to be made from the treated veneers. In the U.S.A., a short period of immersion in 5 per cent borax at 130°F has been found to prevent attack by some of the smaller species of *Lyctus*.

Where stacks of timber are found to be infested and facilities for heat treatment are not available insecticide treatment may be attempted, but it cannot be relied on to give 100 per cent eradication.

Since *Lyctus* larvæ can develop only in wood that contains starch, any treatment that removes this foodstuff from the wood will render the latter immune from their attack. For instance, if the cells of the sapwood are kept in a moist condition for a few months after felling they will use up their stores of starch, and the timber will then be safe from attack. The starch content of the sapwood will be greatly reduced if the logs are left to lie from four to six months before they are sawn up, as the living cells will continue to respire, and will gradually use up their reserves of starch. However, while such delay in the conversion of the log may be advantageous from the point of view of avoiding *Lyctus* damage, there is a grave risk that in the meantime it will become infected with fungi. Experiments have been carried out to find if girdling the trees will result in sufficient depletion of starch to render them immune, but so far the results obtained have been somewhat inconclusive.

It has been suggested that kiln drying, by killing the living cells in the sapwood and thereby fixing the starch in the wood, does in fact increase its liability to subsequent infestation by *Lyctus*. But this is true only when relatively higher temperatures are used for fast drying of hardwoods such as Obeche. In the kiln drying of Oak and Ash the first stages are carried out at comparatively low temperatures of about 40°C which would favour starch depletion and, in consequence, diminish the risk of *Lyctus* attack. Kiln drying of timber known to be already infested with *Lyctus* is a very useful method of ensuring that the wood is free from the infection; and timber sterilized in this way can be protected against reinfestation by the application of an insecticide. In timber up to one inch thick *Lyctus* Beetles at all stages can be killed by exposure to a temperature of 130°F in a saturated atmosphere (100 per cent relative humidity) for $2\,^1/_2$ hours. Proportionally longer times are necessary for thicker material. If, for any reasons it is difficult or undesirable to expose the timber to this temperature and the very high humidity, effective sterilization can be achieved by exposing it for much longer periods at slightly lower temperatures in relative humidities of only 60 or 80 per cent. A detailed schedule for heat sterilization of *Lyctus* infested timber is given in Forest Products Research Leaflet No. 13. When furniture or joinery *in situ* is found to be infested treatment should follow the lines suggested for control of the Common Furniture Beetle. (See below.) Since damage of *Lyctus* is sometimes confused with the attacks of Pinhole Borers the characteristic features of each are given in Table 4.

Furniture Beetles—Anobiidae

The Furniture Beetles are essentially pests of old, seasoned timber, and some of them have a definite preference for wood already partially decayed. Their natural habitat is the dead and decaying branches of trees such as Oak and Willow. They attack both soft and hard woods, and some of them are very common and exceedingly troublesome as pests of furniture and woodwork in buildings. In this country two are of outstanding importance—the Death-Watch Beetle and the Common Furniture Beetle. The former has not yet been found in Scotland and is exceedingly rare in Ireland, while the latter is common in all parts of the British Isles, but is probably most troublesome in the western, more humid parts of the country.

Death-Watch Beetle—Xestobium rufovillosum. This beetle has achieved more notoriety in this country than any other wood-boring insect. This is partly due to its sinister name, and partly on account of the fact that it has attacked and caused serious damage to the woodwork of so many ancient and famous buildings. It gets its name from an old superstition that the tapping sounds made by the beetles presaged a death in the house where they were heard. The noise is produced by the adult beetles striking their heads on the surface of the wood during the mating season (April-June) and appears to be the beetles' way of calling to their mates. The tapping is never continuous; usually four or five taps are given in rapid succession and then there is a short interval of some minutes before tapping is resumed.

The Death-Watch Beetle confines its attentions to old seasoned timbers, generally those of some considerable size. It is most commonly found in Oak, but has also been found in Chestnut, Elm and Walnut, and also in softwoods where these have been in contact with infested hardwoods. It occasionally attacks large furniture, such as pews in churches, but is rarely found in ordinary furniture or in small articles.

Widespread public interest in the damage caused by this insect was first aroused when it was found that the magnificent old oak roof of Westminster Hall was severely damaged by its depredations. The late Professor Maxwell Lefroy undertook a comprehensive investigation of its habits, and the methods he devised for its eradication are still the basis of present-day practice. Since then the Death-Watch Beetle has been found to be prevalent in many other important buildings, including York Minster, the Palace of Versailles and Chequers, and also in a host of country churches and manor houses. It is comparatively rare in small houses and cottages.

The adult beetle is a small thickset insect, $^1/_4$ to $^1/_2$ in. in length, dark brown in colour, and coated in patches with short yellowish hairs. (See Fig. 18.) It is a sluggish little creature and has seldom been seen to fly, though it may open its wings to break its fall from a roof. The larva is a curved white grub, covered with fine, long, yellowish hairs; it has a yellowish brown head furnished with dark brown jaws. The length of its life as a grub seems to depend on the condition of the timber in which it is feeding. In decayed wood, under optimum conditions, the life cycle from egg to beetle may be completed in a year, but in sound timber, under less favourable conditions, it may spend three of four years in the wood, and instances have been known of its living in the grub stage for ten years or more. The larva when fully grown pupates at the end of the summer, and after two or three weeks casts its pupal skin. The beetle, however, remains in the wood till the following spring when it emerges to mate. The exit holes made on the surface of the wood are round, and measure about $^1/_8$ in. across. (See Fig. 19.) The workings of the Death-Watch Beetle can be distinguished from those of other beetles by the presence in the frass (bore dust) of small round pellets or granules, which give the dust a gritty feel to the touch.

Eradication of the Death-Watch Beetle presents considerable

Fig. 19. Damage in Oak caused by Death-Watch Beetle.
Scale shown.

difficulties as the larvæ are often so deeply embedded in the wood that they are beyond the reach of insecticidal treatment. Attacks often die out for no apparent reason before all the wood is consumed, so when an outbreak is discovered the first thing to do is to try to find whether live insects are still present. Fresh bore dust and clean newly-formed exit holes are indications of activity, and the degree of infestation can sometimes be gauged by the number of beetles found on the floor of the building during the period of emergence. When extensive damage is found, it is generally the result of many years' infestation, as the rate of working is always slow, and under fairly dry conditions may be extremely so.

When timber in a building is found to be infested a thorough inspection of the timbers should at once be made, paying particular attention to the ends of beams embedded in the walls. Any timber showing fungal decay should be removed as this is particularly liable to attack, and sources of dampness should be sought and dealt with. Severely attacked structural timbers in which active infestation is found should be replaced, but the timbers found in old buildings are often of such generous proportions that an ample margin of safety may remain even after the cross-section has been reduced by insect attack, and drastic structural alterations may not be necessary, provided that further damage is prevented. Softened wood on the surface should be cut away with a draw knife, and superficial dust and dirt removed with a vacuum cleaner. Two thorough applications of an insecticide (See below) should be given, preferably during the early summer. It is desirable that the application should be repeated during this period for several consecutive years, but where it is necessary to erect scaffolding, as for treating a roof, this may prove unduly costly. In such cases an effort should be made to inject the insecticide with a pressure sprayer into all the holes, cracks and joints of the wood. Collection and destruction of the beetles during the period of emergence is worth while, as many will be caught before they have laid their eggs; and regular inspection of the affected timbers should be made for several years after treatment. When carrying out repairs only well-seasoned oak heartwood, or softwood that has been impregnated under pressure, should be used for replacements.

Attack by the Death-Watch Beetle can largely be prevented by keeping the roofs and guttering in a good state of repair, so as to ensure that no fungal decay occurs, and by providing ventilation around the ends of built-in beams. If old timber is used in a new construction, or in repairs, it should be very carefully examined for signs of insect damage, and if there are any doubts as to its soundness, it should be sterilized by heat treatment in a kiln. (See above under *Lyctus*.)

Common Furniture Beetle—Anobium punctatum. In New Zealand this insect is known as the Common House Borer, and this is perhaps a more appropriate name than the one used in England. Not only is it a menace to old furniture, but it is also extremely common in flooring and roof timbers in houses, and there are probably few buildings over a certain age which do not contain some traces of its damage.

This is by far the commonest wood-boring insect in the British Isles, and it is now widely distributed throughout the temperate regions of the world. The damage which it causes to timber indoors in Great Britain is on the aggregate greater than that caused by all the other species put together. One authority maintains that it is responsible for about 80 per cent of the total damage caused by wood-boring insects in this country.

It is most prevalent in coastal areas, and in island countries such as the British Isles and New Zealand, where the average relative humidity of the air throughout the year tends to be higher than in countries possessing continental climates. The fact that commercial surveys often show a high incidence of woodworm in the south-east of England is due to the fact that there is a greater density of houses in this area; and also that the owners are mostly better able to afford to have their houses surveyed and repaired. Whereas in the more agricultural western districts little notice may be taken of the presence of beetle holes in the woodwork.

There is some evidence that this insect has become more prevalent in England during the past few decades, and it has certainly spread appreciably in South Africa. Probably a major reason for its increase is that there is a much higher proportion of susceptible sapwood in the building timbers that have been used since 1920. In Europe the general lack of building maintenance during the war years also no doubt encouraged its spread, and the shutting up of houses and the storage of furniture for long periods at this time were other contributory causes.

The natural home of the Furniture Beetle is in the dead and decaying parts of old hardwood trees and shrubs. In buildings, however, it seems to be equally happy in softwoods. The wood from many different temperate trees may be attacked but that from Rosaceous fruit trees is particularly susceptible. In all timbers in which there is a definite coloured heartwood the attack is generally confined to the sapwood. There are no records of its attacking the tropical light hardwoods which have been used so extensively for the manufacture of furniture and joinery. Birch plywood bonded with animal glue is particularly susceptible to infestation—doubtless this type of glue supplies the much needed protein which is lacking in the wood— but plywood bonded with synthetic resin adhesives appears to be immune to attack.

Because infestations by *Anobium* were never observed in newly built houses it was thought until recently that freshly felled timber was not susceptible to their attack. However, investigations at Princes Risborough and elsewhere have proved that freshly felled wood of the appropriate kind (Scots Pine sapwood for example) is readily attacked and may in fact be more suitable for the development of the larvæ than is really old wood. The last formed annual rings next to the bark appear to provide the most favourable conditions for larvæ development, and this may well be related to the somewhat higher nitrogen content of the outermost zone of sapwood. Bletchly has concluded that cell contents play an important role in the nutrition of *Anobium* since extraction of the wood with water reduces its suitability for larval growth.

Though *Anobium* larvæ (unlike those of *Xestobium*) are able to establish themselves in perfectly sound wood, fungal decay does increase the susceptibility of some timbers to attack. The larvæ establish themselves more easily in the decayed and softened wood which appears, possibly on account of its enhanced nitrogen content, to nourish them better than does sound wood.

While it is possible for dry timber containing only 12-15 per cent of moisture to become infested this beetle definitely prefers rather damper conditions and attack is likely to be most severe in poorly ventilated, damp situations. The larvæ grow most rapidly in wood that is at the fibre saturation point. Newly-hatched larvæ will not develop in wood held at a relative humidity below 65-70 per cent but larger larvæ can tolerate slightly dryer conditions. The larvæ of *Anobium* develop best in somewhat cooler conditions than those of other wood-borers, such as *Hylotropes*. It is therefore easy to understand why *Anobium* is not such a serious pest in the dry, centrally-heated houses of the United States and Canada as it is in Western Europe and New Zealand, and why it has never yet been found in the tropics.

The adult Furniture Beetle is a small, fat, dark brown creature, $\frac{1}{10}$ to $\frac{1}{5}$ in. in length. (See Fig. 18.) Freshly emerged specimens have a covering of fine yellowish hairs. A characteristic feature is the "hooding" of the head by the pro-thorax. The wing cases are marked with lines of small pits. The larvæ are small, whitish, curved grubs, also covered with fine, short, yellowish hairs. When mature they measure about $1/4$ in. in length. The head is yellowish brown and the jaws are dark brown.

The beetles emerge from the wood during the summer and, after mating, the female beetle lays about 20 oval, whitish eggs in cracks, crevices, and open joints in the wood. These hatch in four to five weeks and the larvæ at once begin to tunnel into the wood, at first parallel to the grain, but later in all directions. The tunnels, which increase in size as the larvæ grow, become filled with a granular frass (bore dust) which, on examination with a lens, can be seen to contain quantities of small, oval or cylindrical fæcal pellets (compare round pellets of Death-Watch Beetle). The larvæ can grow to full size within a year in decayed wood in the open, but under dryer, less favourable conditions they may spend two or three years, or even longer, in the wood before they pupate. After a few weeks in the pupal state the beetles bore their way to the surface, making exit holes about $^1/_{16}$ in. across. (See Fig. 20.) The beetles are much more active

Fig. 20. Damage caused by Common Furniture Beetle. Scale shown.

than the Death-Watch and fly readily, especially in warm weather; thus infestation can be spread to different parts of a building or from one building to another.

Treatment and Remedial Measures. When Furniture Beetle

101

H

damage is discovered the first thing to do is to determine how extensive it is, and whether active living insects are present. Piles of fresh bore dust and the presence of clean, newly-bored exit holes are certain indications of current activity. In structural timbers such as rafters, larvæ can be sought in the wood by gradually cutting away the decomposed layers on the surface with a draw knife. It is very common to find evidence of old damage in flooring in which all activity has ceased and the beetles long since departed. It is possible that sometimes the beetle population is reduced by the action of parasites and predators, which attack the grubs of the wood-boring beetles.

Furniture and small articles can be rid of infection by fumigation with a gas toxic to insects. Since the gases normally employed, i.e. hydrogen cyanide and methyl bromide, are also poisonous to human beings, the treatment should be carried out by specialist firms, and should never be attempted at home. Fumigation is particularly suitable for treatment of valuable objects such as violins, pictures and carvings, the tone or appearance of which might be affected by treatment with an insecticide. It does not, however, afford any protection against subsequent reinfestation.

Exposure for a sufficient length of time to temperatures above the lethal for the insects will effectively rid woodwork of infestation, but in applying the heat great care must be taken not to dry out the timber so much that severe shrinkage and consequent splitting will be the result. The treatment, except in the case of quite small articles, should be carried out in a timber-drying kiln provided with properly controlled means of humidifying the atmosphere. Exposure to a temperature of 130°F at a relative humidity of 80 per cent should have no deleterious effect on polished surfaces. Sterilization of complete roofs by injection of hot air has been suggested for eradication of furniture and Death-Watch Beetles from roofing timbers; but though this process has been used on the Continent for treatment of roofs infested with House Longhorn, it has never yet been undertaken on a practical scale in this country.

Dielectric heating, employing high frequency fields in the range of 76 and 37 Mc/s, has been used succesfully to sterilize timber infested with insects such as *Lyctus* and *Anobium* larvæ. Exposure to such a field strength of 1000 V for periods as short as one minute may raise the internal temperature sufficiently to kill all the larvæ present. Timbers up to 10 in. thick can probably be treated where electrodes can be applied to both sides of the wood. Panelling up to one inch thick can be treated from one side only by means of so-called "stray field" h.f. heating which provides a unique method for sterilizing wood panelling *in situ* where the back surface is inaccessible.

The most convenient way of treating infested furniture is to apply an insecticide solution (See below) to all parts in which there are exit holes or other signs of infestation. All dust and dirt should be cleaned off, and any leather or textiles removed so as to expose the rough wood underneath, which is the part most likely to be infested. Two or three liberal coats of the fluid should then be applied to all the unpolished surfaces, not forgetting the under surfaces of the legs. If a suitably compounded insecticide is used the fluid can also be brushed liberally over the polished surfaces without any serious ill effects on the polish. To get better penetration of the fluid into the tunnels and intercommunicating galleries, the fluid should also be injected into the flight holes.

Convenient small injectors for this purpose have been designed by manufacturers of insecticides. These have a rubber washer around the nozzle so that pressure can be applied to force the fluid into the tunnels. They are, therefore, much more effective than hypodermic syringes, or fountain-pen fillers, with which fluid can only be poured, or dropped, into the holes. After thorough treatment of the piece the flight holes should be sealed up with plastic wood or wax, which not only helps to

103

keep the insecticide from evaporating but enables any fresh holes to be easily detected.

When surveying the woodwork in a building in which Furniture Beetle has been discovered the condition of the rafters should be carefully tested, and the floor boards taken up in places for the condition of the joists to be examined. If the roof timbers are found to contain active infestation the softened, disintegrated sapwood should be removed from the rafters by means of a draw knife, and the whole roof should be thoroughly cleaned before any insecticidal treatment is applied. Insecticidal solutions can be applied more thoroughly by brush than by spraying, though for large areas and inaccessible crannies spraying is obviously easier and more economical. There are now a number of efficient specialist firms operating in different parts of the country. If a householder finds that he is confronted with an extensive outbreak he would be well advised to consult one of these, obtaining quotations from several independent firms before deciding which to employ. If only a few boards or joists are involved he will probably find it less expensive to carry out the treatment himself.

Insecticides suitable for use against woodworm

An insecticide, to be effective, should combine high toxicity, or killing power, against the insects concerned, with good powers of penetration, and it should contain ingredients that will persist in the wood to give protection against reinfestation. For some purposes absence of colour may also be important. Creosote, and products derived from it, are perhaps not so effective as some other compounds, but on account of their relatively low cost can be recommended for treatment of woodwork in barns, sheds and garages.

There are now on the market a number of effective proprietary insecticides for use against woodworm, and these can, in general, be recommended in preference to paraffin or turpentine which only kill those insects with which they come into direct contact, whereas the insecticides give off fumes toxic to the insects which can penetrate the wood to greater depths and more uniformly than the liquids themselves.

Orthodichlorobenzene formed the basis of a number of the older insecticides. It combines high toxicity to insects with good penetrating power, but it soon evaporates from the treated wood, and if protection against reinfestation is required it should be used in combination with less volatile materials. It should be noted that this compound is to some degree toxic to human beings and after its use on woodwork the rooms in question should be well ventilated and left unoccupied for a few weeks.

Chlorinated naphthalenes, metallic naphthenates, and pentachlorophenol are other compounds commonly incorporated in preservative insecticides. Contact insecticides, such as BHC and dieldrin and DDT, are often included in proprietary insecticides to increase their toxicity, but as they are to some degree volatile they may contribute less to the long-term preservative action than do the stomach poisons.

In new constructions, or in carrying out repairs to an existing building, permanent protection to the new timber can be afforded by having it impregnated under pressure with a water-borne preservative.

Ernobius mollis. This borer is an Anobiid beetle which causes damage that is sometimes mistaken for that caused by *Anobium punctatum.* It attacks only softwoods, but it is widely distributed throughout the world and is very common in Scandinavia from whence it probably spread in unbarked logs and boards. The reddish brown beetles, which emerge during the summer, somewhat resemble the Common Furniture Beetle but are slightly larger and have longer antennæ and softer wing covers. (See Fig. 21.)

Ernobius mollis can breed only where bark is present on

105

Fig. 21. *Ernobius mollis*.   C.C.R.
A. Adult beetle.

B. Damage caused by these beetles.

dead timber. The larvæ feed on the inner bark, sometimes boring superficially into the outer sapwood. The frass (bore dust) is therefore mostly dark brown in colour but usually contains a few light coloured pellets. The emerging beetles may bore through solid timber or plywood covering timbers in the bark of which they have developed.

Attack normally ceases after a few years when the bark peels off, and no remedial or insecticidal treatment is required in the affected structural timbers and joinery. However, to avoid alarm among householders it is wise always to remove all bark from the waney edges of rafters or joists. Bark should also be removed from softwood boards used for packing-cases, otherwise the emerging beetles may damage the contents of the cases.

Wharf Borer—Nacerdes melanura. This insect is not considered to be a primary pest of sound timber, but it attacks softwoods and hardwoods that have been affected by some form of fungal decay, and are in a moist condition. Typically this insect is found in timbers that have been wetted by sea water, being found a few feet above high water mark. It also occurs in timber along canals and other fresh water areas. Occasionally it is found in very damp timber in the basements of buildings and around lavatory pans.

The adult beetle is $1/4$ to $1/2$ in. in length, yellowish brown in colour with dark tips to the wing covers. The whole body is covered with a yellowish pubescence. The larva, unlike that of most of the other wood borers, is slender and $1/2$-$1\frac{1}{4}$ in. long with a large yellowish head and three pairs of moderately long legs.

Wood-boring Weevils—Cossonidæ. There are a number of insects that attack timber only after it has been decayed and of these the Wood-boring Weevils are perhaps the commonest. These are small brown beetles, about the size of the Common Furniture Beetle, but distinguished from it by the possession

TABLE 4

Table of Characteristics for distinguishing
some of the Commoner Wood-boring Beetles

Insect	Timbers attacked	Exit holes	Bore dust
Common Furniture Beetle.	Seasoned hardwoods and softwoods, sound or decayed. Usually sapwood only.	Circular. Approx. $\frac{1}{16}$ in. diameter.	Ellipsoidal pellets.
Death-Watch Beetle.	Old decayed hardwoods; softwoods rarely. Heartwood and sapwood.	Circular. Approx. $\frac{1}{8}$ in. diameter.	Coarse, bun-shaped pellets.
Lyctus Powder-post Beetle.	Seasoned and partly seasoned sound hardwoods. Usually sapwood only but emergence may occur through heartwood.	Circular. Approx. $\frac{1}{16}$ in. diameter.	Fine talcum-like powder.
House Longhorn Beetle.	Seasoned sound softwoods, usually sapwood only.	Oval. Approx. $\frac{1}{4}$ in. $\times$ $\frac{1}{8}$ in. diameter.	Larger compact cylindrical pellets and powder.
Ambrosia (Pinhole Borer) Beetles.	Unseasoned sound hardwoods and softwoods.	Circular (entrance holes). Variable in diameter according to species of insect, but approx. $\frac{1}{50}$-$\frac{1}{8}$ in. in diameter.	Absent, but tunnels darkly stained, the stain sometimes spreading into surrounding wood.
Wood-boring Weevils.	Seasoned hardwoods and softwoods, decayed or very damp.	Irregularly oval, of varying size, approx. $\frac{1}{32}$ $\times$ $\frac{1}{16}$ in.	Ellipsoidal pellets smaller than those produced by fullgrown *Anobium* larvae.

of the short snout, characteristic of most weevils. The damage they cause is similar to that of the Furniture Beetles, but the tunnels are smaller, and the exit holes are oval and less well defined. They require really damp conditions for their development and are almost invariably found in wood affected with fungal decay of the so-called "wet rot" type. (See page 186.) Their appearance can therefore be prevented by ensuring that fungal decay does not occur. If the weevils should appear their further spread can be checked by the removal of the decayed wood and by drying out of the timber.

HYMENOPTERA

Though there are only a few wood-boring insects in this large group, which includes the bees, wasps and true ants, the Wood Wasps are worthy of mention. Two species are not uncommon in Great Britain, *Urocerus gigas* and *Sirex cyaneus*; other species occur in America. They only attack trees of the Pinaceae family.

Urocerus gigas. The Giant Wood Wasp, as this creature is commonly called, is a large striking looking insect, up to 1 $^3/_4$ in. long and black and gold in colour. It is sometimes mistaken for a hornet as it has a formidable appearance, and the female is provided with a long ovipositor (up to $^3/_4$ in. long) which could easily be mistaken for a sting. These insects are quite harmless to man but their sudden emergence from furniture or woodwork may occasion alarm.

Sirex cyaneus. This, the Steel-blue Wood Wasp, is a smaller species than the Giant Wood Wasp, measuring only $^1/_2$ to $^3/_4$ in. in length. It is common in Larch and Silver Fir woods. (See Fig. 22.)

Both these Wood Wasps are forest insects which infest logs and sickly standing, trees in which the sap flow is defective. The female bores into the wood with her saw-like ovipositor and deposits the egg deeply in the wood. The eggs have been shown to carry spores of a fungus (*Stereum* sp.) which grows out into the wood before the larvæ hatch and is thought to render it more suitable for their development. The larvæ of both species are white, with a pale brownish head, and have three pairs of short stumpy legs. At the end of the body

Fig. 22. Steel-blue Wood Wasp, *Sirex cyaneus*. *Above*: Female ovipositing in Larch. Enlarged 4 times. *Below*: Damage caused by *Sirex* sp. in Silver Fir, showing exit holes and larval tunnels.

there is a sharp spine with which the larva packs the frass behind it in the tunnel. The larva may spend from two and a half to three years in the wood before it pupates in a cell about $1/_2$ in. below the surface. After five to six weeks pupation the adult wasp emerges through a circular exit hole. (See Fig. 22.) There is no risk of *Sirex* wasps reinfesting seasoned timber, and the damage which they do nearly always originates in the forest.

Infestation of softwoods by Wood Wasps recently became a matter of concern to European exporters to Australia. Stringent quarantine regulations were imposed by that country with the object of excluding these insects which were thought to constitute a possible menace to the large pine plantations. Investigations by the Forest Products Research Laboratory have shown that the Siricid wasps and their larvæ are very resistant to methyl bromide and that sterilization by fumigation of sawn timber and packing-cases with this gas was unlikely to be completely effective—at any rate at the dosages commonly recommended. The only certain treatment seems to be a short period of exposure to heat in a kiln.

Few other members of the *Hymenoptera* are important as pests of timber, but occasionally solitary bees tunnel into decayed wood and construct therein cells for their eggs about the size of a small revolver bullet, made of carefully folded pieces of leaf. Ants are sometimes found working in badly decayed wood, but no true ant causes serious damage to timber in Great Britain.

LEPIDOPTERA (BUTTERFLIES AND MOTHS)

The characteristic features of the *Lepidoptera* are the possession of four membranous wings, almost completely covered with overlapping scales which render them opaque; and mouth parts which, in the larvæ, are designed for biting

111

and in the adult for sucking. They undergo complete meta-morphosis.

The larvæ of one group of moths, known as the Carpenter Moths, bore in trees and can sometimes cause quite serious damage. The Goat Moth (*Cossus cossus*), so called from its strong and rather objectionable odour which can be smelt even outside the tree where it is working, is one of the largest British moths, sometimes having a wing span of $3^1/_2$ in. It is greyish brown in colour, and has a stoutly built body. The caterpillar, which may reach a length of 3 in., has distinctive coloraticn, the head and first segment being dark brown, and the dorsal surface of the remaining segments purplish red, while the rest of the body is flesh coloured. At first it tunnels between the bark and the wood, and then makes a winding gallery (half to one inch or more wide) in the trunk. The grubs live for two or three years in a tree; later they leave it and build a cocoon in the ground before they pupate. The Goat Moth attacks various broad-leaved trees, particularly Oak, Willow and Poplar, and when present in numbers can cause considerable damage to the wood, rendering the trunk useless. Only in gardens and parks is it worth while attempting to control this pest, and all that can be done is to remove the dead tissue by skilful surgery, and to insert a poison into the tunnels that are left. A little carbon bisulphide should be injected into the hole, or placed in it on a wad of cotton wool. The hole should then be plugged with grafting wax or putty. There is no risk of the grubs continuing to work in timber that has been sawn up and seasoned.

The Leopard Moth (*Zeuzera æsculi*) is a handsome insect, somewhat smaller than the Goat Moth, and has white wings closely spotted with black markings. It has a somewhat similar life history to the Goat Moth, and causes damage to young trees by boring into the branches and weakening them so that they break off in a wind.

CHAPTER 7

Destruction of Wood by Insects 2. Isoptera (Termites)

TERMITES are social insects belonging to the order *Isoptera*. There are no solitary termites. These insects have been called "white ants" because their social organization resembles that of the true ants but, though in many ways they do behave like ants, the two orders are, in fact, quite distinct and unrelated.

Termites occur throughout the tropics and are often thought of as essentially tropical insects. They are, however, quite common in many sub-tropical and warm temperate countries, while a few hardy species survive in countries with quite cold winters, such as Spain, parts of Italy and France, and in America as far north as Vancouver. The greatest number of species occur in tropical rain forests, but perhaps the most striking evidences of their activity are to be found in the open veldt country in Africa and Australia where the termite mounds are a conspicuous feature of the landscape.

Some 1800 species of termites have been described, and these have been classified into varying numbers of families. Morris (1961) suggests six, three of which he again divides into a number of sub-families. Within this great assemblage it is evident that there must be a wide diversity of forms and behaviour, and there must necessarily be many exceptions to any general statements about the group.

A typical termite colony contains one or more fully developed females, or "queens"; a similar number of males; and a very large number of sterile individuals of two types, or castes, known as workers and soldiers.

The worker ants may be regarded as individuals of either sex which have not developed to reproductive maturity. They are soft bodied and wingless and live sheltered lives in the ground or inside the piece of wood on which they are feeding. They possess saw-toothed jaws suited to cutting through wood, and they carry out foraging and building operations. (See Fig. 23.)

The soldiers' task, as their name implies, is to defend the colony against invaders such as the true ants, which are their most deadly enemies. Their bodies are well adapted for this purpose as they have large heads with which they can block the entrance to a tunnel against an invader, and their jaws are

Fig. 23. Drywood Termites, *Neotermes jouteli*. Showing eggs, young and older nymphs, a soldier, a queen, and the distinctive frass.

useful in fighting being pincer or sabre-like. In some species the soldiers can also exude from their heads a sticky acid which can be directed at the waist of an attacking ant, gumming it up and rendering it powerless.

The winged adult reproductives are rarely seen as they mate soon after emerging from their nests and then shed their wings and return to obscurity. They are always some shade of dull brown, and they vary in size from large African species $^3/_4$ in. long down to small Eastern species only $^1/_4$ in. in length. Within one colony normally only one pair, the "king" and the "queen" are actively reproductive, though they are sometimes assisted in their task of maintaining the population by supplementary reproductives, one of whom may acquire the status of queen should the latter be killed.

The queen may live for many years and may reach quite a large size, with an immensely distended abdomen, several inches in length, containing the highly developed ovaries from which an egg may be discharged every few seconds. The output of eggs sometimes reaches the astounding figure of 30,000 per day, so that during her life-time a queen may lay literally millions of eggs. Her ability to lay develops as the number of attendants available to feed and groom her and to deal with the eggs increases. In the royal chamber the queen and her consort are constantly guarded by soldiers.

CLASSIFICATION OF TERMITES

From a practical point of view it is most convenient to classify termites according to their habits and mode of life. They can thus be divided into two main groups depending on whether they maintain direct contact with the ground or live completely isolated from it. The former may be called "Earth-dwelling Termites" because they live either wholly or partly, in the ground, and always maintain a connection with the soil

115

even when their nests are above ground level. The second group, the "Wood-dwelling Termites", spend their lives

Fig. 24. Mound in Uganda built by the termite *Macrotermes natalensis*.

in wood and the colonies are started by a mating pair entering wood above the ground level.

The earth-dwelling group can be subdivided into:

    (1) Subterranean termites

    (2) Mound building termites

    (3) Carton-nest building termites.

The wood-dwelling types can be classed as:

    (1) Dry wood termites

    (2) Damp wood termites.

Earth-dwelling Termites
    Subterranean. These insects live and build their nests in

116

Fig. 25. Roof beams in a building on the East African coast damaged by the termite *Coptotermes amanii*.

the ground, and wehn they come out in search of food they invariably build earthen tunnels to reach the wood or other palatable food materials which they require. They can construct these tunnels with surprising rapidity, over concrete, or over treated timber in order to reach untreated timber higher up. Once the tunnels have been made the workers are completely protected, against desiccation as well as against their enemies, in their passage from the nest up to the chosen food supply.

117

It seems to be essential for these insects to maintain contact with moist ground and they take energetic steps to repair their tunnels whenever they are damaged. When it is possible they attack timber from behind or within, excavating and hollowing out the wood but carefully avoiding its surface, which therefore remains intact. (See Fig. 25).

Subterranean Termites are the most widely distributed of all the forms, and it has been estimated that they cause 95 per cent of all the damage attributed to termites.

Mound-building. These insects build their nests above the ground. They use particles of sand or excrement cemented together with their saliva to construct quite large mounds. The size and shape varies according to the species that builds them. The so-called "white ant hills" are a conspicuous feature of the landscape in parts of Africa, Asia and Australia. In Equatorial Africa domes may be found having a diameter of 40 ft and a height of 12 ft, while the steeple-shaped constructions of some of the species of *Macrotermes* may attain heights up to 30 ft. (See Fig. 24.)

Inside the mounds there may be a honeycomb of small cells or a series of horizontal floors supported on pillars. Often the chambers inside contain the so-called "fungus gardens" in which the termites cultivate fungi on a spongy mass of chewed-up fragments of wood. The inhabitants of the mound regularly crop the growths of these fungi which appear to constitute an important part of their diet. Some of the fungi (e.g. *Termitomyces* sp.) growing in these "gardens" are not found elsewhere and have evolved in response to the special conditions in the "ant hills".

Mound-building Termites are not usually such a menace to buildings as are the subterranean species but the removal of their mounds sometimes presents a civil engineering problem in the Equatorial Zone of Africa where *Macrotermes goliath* flourishes. Shattering the mounds with numerous small charges of gelignite followed by bulldozing is often the only way to level the mounds economically. The use of explosive has an additional advantage in that it kills off most of the termites that are in the mound.

Carton-nest Building. The nests of these Termites are composed of a material, known as carton, which is made from woody fragments, particles of soil and excrement. This type of nest may be built on the ground or in the forks of trees or on wooden structures, but wherever it is, the inhabitants always maintain contact with the ground and gain access to buildings under cover of earthen tunnels.

Wood-dwelling Termites

Dry Wood Dwellers. These insects live in dry seasoned wood and do not require to have any connection with the ground. They are not so common as the subterranean types but, when they do occur, they may present a serious problem. Their entry into buildings cannot be checked by shields on the foundations as the adults can fly in at open windows and infest timber remote from the ground. Some of the most serious pests of buildings belong to this group which includes *Cryptotermes brevis*, the West Indian Dry Wood Termite. This latter insect, which is widely distributed throughout the Caribbean and tropical South America, has recently been found in Ghana and round about Durban in South Africa where it has undoubtedly been introduced by man. Other species of *Cryptotermes* are now found in East Africa and Asia and are believed to have been spread by man in quite recent times.

Even Subterranean Termites have been introduced into other countries by man. For instance an Australian subterranean species has now become established in New Zealand.

Damp Wood Dwellers. These can live only in wood that is constantly moist. They normally inhabit fallen logs and stumps in damp places, and a few species live in growing trees. On the whole the members of this group are unimportant so far as buildings are concerned.

NUTRITION OF TERMITES AND THEIR DIGESTIVE PROCESSES

The range of organic materials attacked by termites is extraordinarily wide but their basic foodstuff is cellulose which they obtain from wood and from other plant materials. Many of the more primitive species digest this with the help of microscopic protozoa in their gut.

Living plants are seldom attacked by termites unless they have already been damaged in some way, as during transplanting operations or by pruning or careless cultivation. They occasionally attack newly-planted sugar cane, clove bushes and certain forest tree seedlings, but, except in the case of certain Eucalyptus plantations, particularly in East Africa, termites cannot be regarded as serious forest pests. Generally speaking termite attack on standing trees is secondary to other forms of damage.

Felled and worked timber and woody debris are the staple diet of most of the termites, but they also sometimes get nourishment from such cellulose containing materials as paper, cotton, jute and straw. Growths of fungi from the "gardens" cultivated by certain groups, such as *Macrotermes*, constitute another important element in their diet. They will also eat rubber and silk, and leather (unless it is full chrome-tanned). Plastics are occasionally attacked, some, such as cellulose acetate, appearing to be positively attractive to some species, while others are probably bored into only incidentally. Surprisingly enough, damage to such insulating materials as neoprene rubber and polyvinyl chloride coverings have been reported in a number of countries.

120

PREVENTION OF TERMITE ATTACK

Attack by Earth-dwelling Termites can be prevented by denying the insects access to a building, but attack on structural timbers by Dry Wood Termites can only be prevented with certainty by thorough preservative treatment of all susceptible timbers, or by the use of naturally durable ones.

Before putting up a building in an area where there is a

Fig. 26. Example of Termite damage from Singapore showing excavations.

TIMBER PESTS AND DISEASES

risk of termite attack the site should be cleared of all woody fragments, tree roots, etc. If the area is known to be infested the ground should be sterilized after the top soil has been removed, by methodically watering the site very thoroughly with an insecticidal solution. Suitable solutions would be:

> 5 per cent sodium pentachlorophenate in water
> 1.0 per cent gamma benzene hexachloride (chlordane)
> 5 per cent dieldrin in fuel oil.

Since Earth-dwelling Termites can gain access to a building only by crawling up from the ground the provision of an impermeable barrier, of bitumen for example, will prevent their entering through walls or foundations. But this barrier must be truly impervious as they have a wonderful ability for finding any weak spot, and will make their way through fine cracks in badly laid concrete. The addition of a small amount of an emulsion of dieldrin to the water used in making the concrete for covering the site has given some promising results. The idea is that any cracks that may form would thus be protected against the passage of termites. Sufficient dieldrin should be added to give about 0.5 per cent of this chemical in the water.

As these termites can cross exposed surfaces of walls, piers and stanchions only under cover of an earthen tunnel, it is most important that all such surfaces should be open to inspection so that any tunnels can be easily spotted and quickly removed. The provision of down-sloping, cone-shaped guards fitted tightly around piers or pipes above ground will effectively prevent the building of tunnels up these, as the insects cannot construct them around knife-edged corners. (See Fig. 27.) Regular inspections should also be made of the supports below any suspended floor so as to detect mounds that may be built up under them.

Care must always be taken to avoid the formation of any

accidental bridges between the soil and the building which would give the termites a chance to cross over. Trees and shrubs growing close to a building may easily provide such access, and steps, handrails and porches often provide contact between soil and building which the insects are quick to make use of. It is always wise to construct outside steps in such

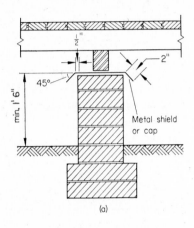

(a)

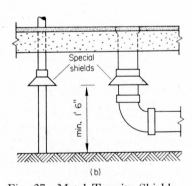

(b)

Fig. 27. Metal Termite Shields.
(a) On dwarf wall below joists.
(b) On drainage pipes under
     building.

123

a way that a gap of at least two inches is left between them and the house.

When solid concrete floors are laid it is advisable not to make the concrete in one piece with the foundations as cracks usually develop where the floors join the walls. It is better to leave a small gap and fill this afterwards with bitumen which resists the entry of termites.

In areas where Dry Wood Termites are present it is much more difficult to protect buildings against infestation as the winged forms fly in through open doors and windows and settle in obscure corners of the woodwork where they establish a colony. They generally avoid painted and polished surfaces and enter rough wood usually through cracks and joints. Severe and quite extensive damage may be done before the infestation is detected.

An unmistakable and distinguishing indication of infestation of Dry Wood Termites is the presence of their fæcal pellets, which are small, hard, seed-like objects with distinct surface markings. These will be found in little heaps somewhere immediately below the infested wood.

In the tropics it is obviously very difficult to screen all openings into a building effectively enough to ensure that no insects can enter. It is however well worth screening with metal gauze all openings into roof spaces, and any rooms that are not in regular use.

In regions where Dry Wood Termites occur it is wise to use only timbers that are naturally resistant to termite attack, or else wood that has been effectively impregnated with a preservative. Even in the absence of Dry Wood Termites the use of naturally durable timbers is a very good second line of defence against the other species.

Termite-resistant Timbers

No timber is wholly and permanently immune from termite

attack, but the heartwood of some species is very resistant and is unlikly to be attacked in a building. The supply of these naturally durable timbers has become exhausted in many countries, such as New Zealand, and even when it is available it is sometimes more economical to use thoroughly treated softwoods because the durable hardwoods are often more difficult to work.

The following list of durable timbers, which is classified by geographical regions, is by no means complete but contains the major species reputed to be resistant to termites in the regions concerned. They are listed under their botanical and trade names, but many also possess other vernacular names.

AFRICA, WEST

Botanical Name	Trade Name
Afzelia africana	Afzelia
Afzelia bipendensis	Afzelia
Albizzia ferruginea	Albizzia
Borassus aethiopium	Rhum palm
Chlorophora excelsa	Iroko
Cyclodiscus gabunensis	Okan
Erythropleum guineense	Missandra
Lophira alata	Ekki
Piptadenia africanum	Dahoma
Pterocarpus soyauxii	African Padauk
Sarcocephalus diderichii	Opepe

AFRICA, EAST AND CENTRAL

Afrormosia angolensis	Afrormosia
Afzelia quanzensis	Afzelia
Baikiaea plurijuga	Rhodesian teak
Brachylaena hutchinsii	Muhuhu
Chlorophora excelsa	Mvule (Iroko)
Juniperus procera	Pencil cedar
Olea welwitschii	Elgon olive (Loliondo)
Pterocarpus angolensis	Muninga
Pygeum africanum	Mueri

125

WEST INDIES AND TROPICAL AMERICA

Botanical Name	Trade Name
Achras sapodilla	Sapodilla
Calophyllum brasiliense	Santa Maria
Cedrela mexicana	Central American cedar
Chlorophora tinctoria	Fustic
Dicorynia sp.	Basralocus
Eperua falcata	Wallaba
Hymenaea courbaril	Courbaril
Mimusops balata	Ballata
Mora excelsa	Mora
Ocotea rodiaei	Greenheart
Peltogyne pubescens	Purpleheart

INDIA, BURMA AND MALAYA

Adina cordifolia	Haldu
Cedrela toona	Burma cedar
Dalbergia latifolia	Indian rosewood
Hopea odorata (and other spp.)	Thingan
Intsia spp.	Merbau
Pterocarpus indicus	Amboyna
Shorea (certain spp. only)	Meranti and Seraya
Tectona grandis	Teak

AUSTRALASIA

Eucalyptus crebra	Ironbark
Eucalyptus marginata	Jarrah
Eucalyptus sideroxylon	Ironbark
Tristania conferta	Brush Box

Some of the above woods are available in Great Britain and manufacturers of articles that are to be exported to countries in which Dry Wood Termites are known to be prevalent would be well advised to use such woods for wooden fittings and any wooden objects of permanent value. Packing-cases that may be stored for any length of time, such as ammunition boxes and other military stores, may require preservative treatment.

It will have been noted that most of the above listed species are heavy hardwoods few of which can readily be worked with hand tools, or conveniently used for joinery or light carcassing work. For such purposes treated softwoods are often preferable and cheaper. Any preservative treatment that is to afford permanent protection must result in deep penetration to ensure that untreated wood will not be exposed by splitting, cutting or abrasion, and to provide a reservoir of preservative against losses from the surface. For all timber that is to come into contact with the soil, impregnation with a tar oil, or a non-leaching water-borne preservative such as copper — chrome — arsenic mixture, is essential. For timber that is to be used under cover non-volatile water-borne preservatives, such as those containing boron or fluorides, may give adequate protection. Wall boards, etc. made from wood or other cellulose material should similarly be treated with preservative if they are to be used in countries where Dry Wood Termites are known to exist.

Prevention of attack by the proper use of preservatives when a building is being erected adds very little to the total cost and may avoid much subsequent expense for costly, and possibly, ineffective, repairs.

SPREAD OF TERMITES—PAST AND FUTURE

There is no doubt that some species of termite have become much more widely distributed in the world as a result of human activities. The more highly organized termites are unlikely ever to become established in the temperate regions, but some of the more primitive forms of drywood Kalotermites and the moist wood Rhinotermites have already spread far beyond their original homes. *Reticulitermes flavipes* has been found all the way from the Gulf of Mexico up to the Canadian border, and is now established in the city of Toronto where it has caused considerable public concern. This same insect has been found in old buildings in Hamburg, and near Salzburg in Austria.

Cryptotermes brevis, known in the U.S.A. as the Rough-headed Powder-post Termite, is widely distributed around the Caribbean, and occurs in Florida and Louisiana. It has caused serious damage in Bermuda and is found near the coast in West and South Africa.

Living termites have occasionally been found in timber imported into the British Isles, but no species has ever been known to become established, even locally. Constant vigilance is however necessary as the climate in parts of Great Britain does not differ greatly from that around La Rochelle in France where *Reticulitermes lucifugus* var. *santonensis* is well established, and is quite a pest in orchards and gardens. This insect seems to require very moist conditions for its successful establishment in any building.

Dr Snyder (private communication) expresses the view that the northward spread of Dry Wood Termites is largely due to man taking infested material into hitherto uninfested areas. In the U.S.A. this method of spread applies also in the case of Damp Wood Termites (Zootermopsis). On the other hand he thinks that the northward spread of *Reticulitermes* can be attributed to the recent trend towards milder winters.

ERADICATION OF TERMITES

Once a building has become heavily infested with termites eradication is always difficult and sometimes impossible. It is, therefore, highly desirable that an invasion should be dealt with as soon as possible before the insects have become well established.

The first step is to find out where the termites are entering the building and to break the links between the building and the soil. Any Subterranean Termites left in the building will die if they are prevented from getting back to moist earth. The soil through which the insects pass in order to reach the building should be poisoned. This may involve digging a trench around the foundations, or, if the floor is on a concrete slab, it may mean making holes with a pneumatic drill through the floor slab in order to get the chemicals into the soil below the concrete. A dosage of one gallon of solution per yard of foundation wall has been suggested.

All sound woodwork near ground level should be well treated with a wood preservative. Any wood that has already been damaged by the termites should, of course, be replaced, either with an inert material or by timber that has been impregnated with preservative. If the attack is in an early stage, or if removal of the infested timber would be a very difficult operation, *in situ* eradication may be attempted. This can be done by drilling $1/4$ in. holes into the infested wood every 2-3 ft, going three quarters of the way through the timbers, and puffing a little insecticidal dust into these holes with a garden plant duster. One ounce of powder per 20 holes is probably an adequate dosage. While doing this a cloth should be held tightly round the nozzle to prevent any dust blowing back into the house. The holes should afterwards be carefully plugged up. Sodium fluosilicate powder, or 50 per cent DDT have been used in this way with success. Even if only a few termites are killed directly by the dust the poison will continue to be spread because the dead termites will be eaten by their fellows.

Piecemeal treatment of infected woodwork may succeed in eradicating termites from a building if the work is carried out with sufficient skill and patience, but a more rapid method is to fumigate the whole building. Fumigation with a poison gas should be undertaken only by specialist firms employing trained operatives. In the U.S.A. it is current practice to cover the whole building with a plastic tent and then to introduce methyl bromide at the rate of 3 lb per 1000 ft³ of space. Exposure to the gas for about 24 hr at 70°F should effectively kill all the termites in the building, but to prevent re-infestation all exposed, unpainted wooden surfaces should be treated, after fumigation, with a solvent type wood preservative. Furniture can conveniently be treated in a special fumigation chamber. Afterwards rooms and furniture should be thoroughly aired before they are occupied or used. Certain materials, such as wool, leather, or foam rubber, react with methyl bromide and should be removed from buildings before fumigation, otherwise they may acquire an unpleasant smell.

Finally—it must again be emphasized that there are many hundreds of species of termites that differ greatly in physiological requirements and behaviour, and that generalizations about methods for their control must always be qualified. Local advice about building traditions and the durability of the native timbers should be sought and considered. Damage by termites should never be accepted as inescapable or inevitable. With proper precautions, buildings and their contents can be effectively protected against these pests, but proper maintainance, as well as good construction, must be provided.

CHAPTER 8

Diseases of Standing Trees

MANY of the defects found in sawn timber originate in the standing trees, and the quality and strength of any wood is greatly influenced by the conditions under which the original tree was grown. For instance, the wood from conifers that have grown very quickly, having few rings to the inch and a low proportion of summer wood, is light and weak; while the timber from ring-porous hardwoods, such as Oak, which has grown very slowly, contains many pores and little fibre, and is soft and easy to work compared with quicker-grown material. Injuries to the cambium (growing layer) of a tree may result in irregularities in the grain. Occasionally this may actually improve the appearance of the wood and enhance its value, as in the case of bird's-eye maple in which the irregularities may be due to punctures made in the bark by an insect.

Growing trees, like other plants, are subject to many diseases and pests, some of which may be fatal and kill the tree in a comparatively short time. Others cause progressive decay in the trunk or branches, and may continue for years without any obvious effect on the vigour of the tree, though actually steadily undermining its strength. Eventually it may become so rotten that the branch will break off, or the tree will blow over in a storm. Diseases of the first type which affect the living tissues, the leaves, twigs, or the actively growing cambium or living sapwood, seldom seriously damage the timber in the trunk, and so their study falls outside the scope of this book. Examples of this type are Chestnut blight, which has wiped out the Swet Chestnut in America, and Dutch Elm disease. This last has affected great numbers of trees in Europe, and has been introduced into the United States where it has caused widespread damage to the Elms that have been planted as shade trees in so many of the eastern cities. The wood of trees killed by these diseases may remain sound and serviceable for years after the death of the tree, until eventually it becomes infected by wood-rotting fungi. It is the diseases of the second type which develop in the heartwood (dead tissue) and which seriously damage the timber which we must now consider.

Wood-rotting fungi cannot reach the vulnerable tissues of the wood so long as the roots of the tree remain alive and healthy and the bark is undamaged. It is only when the roots die as the result of unfavourable soil conditions or by the attack of a parasitic fungus, or where wounds expose the wood to infection, that the organisms that cause decay can gain entry to the trunk. The principle is the same as with an animal—the germs that cause blood-poisoning can gain entry into the body only when the protective layer of skin is broken. Decay of the heartwood commonly known as *heart rot*, may develop in any part of the trunk, depending on where the parasitic fungus makes its entry. When infection enters through dead or diseased roots it sets up *butt rot*. When it enters through a branch wound it causes a *top rot*. Butt rot can appear in trees of any age if the roots are in an unhealthy condition, or have received severe wounds at, or near, ground level. Top rot is common only in old trees having branches large enough to contain heartwood.

Butt Rot

In Young Trees

Many plantations of young conifers have been planted in recent years on land that has not borne a forest crop for centuries, such as derelict agricultural land, poor heath land, or peat moors, ın which the soil conditions are unfavourable for the growth of such trees. It is not, therefore, surprising that sometimes the roots have become unhealthy and diseased. On badly drained land trees may grow well for a few years until their roots penetrate down into the waterlogged layers, where they die for lack of air. Equally bad are the sites where there is a hard "pan" in the subsoil which restricts the downward growth of the roots, and the drainage of water during wet weather, so that during a dry spell the tree is unable to draw moisture from the deeper layers below the hard pan.

The existence of widespread butt rot may remain undetected until the first thinnings are made, as at first it may have little or no effect on the vigour of the trees, which may appear to be making quite satisfactory growth, while all the time rot is consuming the inner heartwood at the base of the trunk. There is evidence that removal of thinnings may lead to the spread of butt rot as the stumps of the young trees that have been felled become infected, and the fungus passes from the old stumps to nearby living trees through root connections. It is therefore a wise precaution, when making thinnings in plantations of susceptible species, to brush over the stumps with creosote soon after the young trees are felled.

Larch and Spruce are more liable to become attacked by butt rot than are Pine, Douglas Fir, or young hardwoods. Without more knowledge than we have at present it is extremely difficult to forecast whether trees planted on any particular site will develop heart rot when they begin to mature. Where previous experience has shown that susceptible species such as larch do become affected at an early age in a particular locality more resistant species should be planted there, or the conifers should be planted in mixture with a hardwood such as beech, the leaves from which will form humus, and help to build up a good forest soil. If financial considerations allow, the first crop to be planted on land that has long been treeless should,

133

L

according to some authorities, include broad-leaved trees which will slowly improve the soil.

Trouble with root diseases and butt rot sometimes occurs when young conifers, or fruit trees, are planted in old woodland where there are decaying hardwood stumps infected with the honey fungus. (See below.)

In Old Trees

Whereas conifers are liable to butt rot at a comparatively early age (plantations less than twenty years old are often infected), broad-leaved saplings rarely suffer from it unless they are sprouts from old infected stools. It is, however, common in *old* hardwood trees such as Elm, Beech and Oak, and is particularly common in large trees in parks and hedgerows. The entry of the infection can generally be traced to some wound at, or near, ground level. Parkland trees are very liable to be wounded by grazing cattle, deer or horses, which often strip the bark off in cold weather, when there is not much herbage. Deer are particularly destructive in this way and butt rot seems especially common in parks where deer are allowed to roam among the trees. Damage by rodents can also lead to infection. The roots of hedgerow elms may be injured during ditching operations, as large roots are often severed when ditches are deepened.

Trees on commons and in woods to which the public have access are often injured by misguided people who light fires for their picnics close up to the trunks of the trees, thereby killing a large area of bark, leaving a wound which sooner or later becomes infected with wood-rotting fungi.

Fungi Causing Butt Rot

There are many different fungi which on occasion cause butt rot in severely wounded trees. The majority of cases, however, are the result of infection by one or other of a few common species. Some of these attack both conifers and broad-leaved trees, while others confine their attentions only to one class. Some of these fungi are actively parasitic and are able to infect undamaged, or only very slightly damaged, trees.

Armillaria mellea—Honey Fungus. This fungus is probably the best known of all those that cause butt rot. It is common in many parts of the world, and can cause damage to a great variety of plants, ranging from forest trees to shrubs and even to such plants as iris, strawberry and potato, these last having starchy roots on which it can feed. Though it can live as a saprophyte on dead wood or humus in the soil, it sometimes becomes actively parasitic and attacks the living roots of healthy trees and shrubs.

Fig. 28. Fruit bodies of *Armillaria mellea*, Honey Fungus, on Oak log. Note rings on stalk. × One fifth.

135

The fruiting bodies of the Honey Fungus are typical mushroom-shaped agarics which develop in the autumn in bunches on stumps of trees. The cap varies in size from 2 in. to 7 in. across, and the rather fibrous stalk may be up to six inches long. A characteristic feature is the pale-coloured ring around the stem an inch or two below the cap. (See Fig. 28.) The young fruit bodies in the "button" stage are honey yellow in colour and are covered with short olive-green scales; later they become tawny or pinkish brown. The gills are a whitish flesh

Fig. 29. Bootlace-like rhizomorphs of the Honey Fungus, *Armillaria mellea*. forming a network around a log.

colour, and the spores are white and often fall on to, and cover, the lower fruit bodies and nearby fallen leaves. A characteristic feature of this fungus is its habit of forming *rhizomorphs*. These are long black stands, rather like bootlaces, which can grow through the soil and penetrate under the bark of living trees and shrubs. (See Fig. 29.) Once the strands have penetrated the bark the mycelium spreads out fanwise in a white, fern-like sheet between the bark and the underlying wood. This can quickly encircle a tree and bring about its death. Sometimes the fungus enters through a taproot and causes a cone of flaky white rot in the heartwood without killing the tree. Surrounding and within this decayed area of wood are thin sheets of blackish mycelium which appear as narrow black lines when the infected wood is cut through.

If, during a period of hot dry weather, the leaves of a tree or shrub turn yellow and shrivel suddenly and then the whole plant dies, search should be made under the bark at the collar for the mycelium and strands of the Honey Fungus. The tree may have been infected for some time and yet have managed to keep alive until excessive transpiration during the hot spell caused a demand for more water than the diseased conducting tissue could supply. In such a case an apparently healthy tree will wilt and die quite suddenly. Once a tree is infected with this fungus there is little that can be done to save it, and the best course is to fell it and to grub up and burn the roots. If one plant in a privet hedge succumbs to the disease the adjoining plants soon develop it and the disease can easily run along the whole hedge, each year killing another pair of bushes, one on each side of the infected area.

To prevent spread of the infection by direct contagion in this way, any tree or shrub that has died as a result of attack by *Armillaria mellea* should be cut down, the stump grubbed out, and as many of the roots as possible removed and burnt. Quicklime should then be dusted freely into the cavity and the soil should be sifted and limed heavily before being replaced in the hole. If possible, a tree or shrub of a different kind should be planted in the place of the one that has died. Removal of diseased stumps in this way is obviously only possible in gardens or parks, as the cost of removing all old infected stumps in woodland is normally prohibitive. Therefore, when experience has shown that a particular species which has been planted in old woodlands becomes severely infected by *Armillaria*, some other species should be tried.

This fungus is somewhat erratic in its parasitism, and although it can attack almost any kind of tree if the circumstances are favourable to its growth, or if the trees are growing

137

poorly, it nevertheless often causes no damage at all to a young crop even when the soil is obviously heavily infected. Fruit trees are particularly liable to attack, and there is always a risk of trouble if these trees are planted in cleared woodland in which stumps of old trees remain. A few years ago a large trial ground for fruit trees that had been prepared at a cost of several thousand pounds, in some old woodland in Kent, had to be abandoned on account of the prevalence of *Armillaria mellea*.

Fomes annosus. This is another quite common fungus which attacks a wide range of hosts. It is occasionally found on broad-leaved trees but never becomes epidemic among them. Spruce and Larch, which are often planted on land that is not really suitable for their growth, generally suffer more from its attacks than does Pine. A survey of the incidence of butt rot in conifers in England has shown that over three quarters of the cases of this disease can be attributed to *Fomes annosus*.

The fruiting body of this fungus is a very tough, irregularly shaped bracket, bright brown on top and having a white pore layer beneath. It always develops near the ground and frequently grows around the stalks of grass or bracken.

The first symptom of attack in the wood is an abnormal purplish red discoloration running up in streaks from the butt. Tiny white pockets appear in the discoloured area, and these gradually enlarge until they become small, lens-shaped cavities lined with a white material rather like lint. (See Fig. 30.) In Larch the wood between the cavities remains quite hard and apparently sound, but in Spruce the decayed heartwood may, in the final stage, be reduced to long, brown, fibrous strands, like coconut fibre. Often a core of sound wood is left and the rot is confined to a ring-shaped area, or to sectors of a ring. Even when only a small area of rot is visible on the butt end of a felled log the rot may have spread for ten or twelve feet up the heartwood, rendering it quite useless.

Fig. 30. White pocket rot in Larch caused by *Fomes annosus*.

Though this fungus usually attacks Spruce and Larch it has caused serious damage to young plantations of Scots Pine in East Anglia—infestation generally occurring after the first thinnings have been felled. Treatment of the stumps thus exposed with a fungicide greatly reduces the spread of infection in such cases. A biological method of control which promises to be very effective on Pine has been proposed by Rishbeth. He found that innoculation of the fresh stumps with a suspension of the spores of a saprophytic wood-rotting fungus, *Peniophora gigantea*, effectively prevents their colonization by *Fomes annosus*.

If butt rot due to this fungus is found to be widespread in a plantation it is probably best to fell all the trees, make use of any sound poles, and then replant with a less susceptible species.

There are many other fungi besides the two just described

139

which sometimes cause butt rot; some of these attack a variety of trees while others specialize only on one kind, or on a closely related group of species. Elm is very liable to butt rot caused by the fungus *Fomes ulmarius*. This forms large thick brackets which have a rather lumpy upper surface, and which are exceedingly tough and hard to dislodge. The flesh of the fruit body is a pale cream colour, while the pore layers on the underside are brick red. Oak is occasionally attacked by *Polyporus dryadeus*, which causes a white rot that may extend for a yard

Fig. 31. Fruit bodies of *Polyporous dryadeus* at base of Oak tree suffering from butt rot.

or two up into the trunk. Its fruiting body is a thick pale brown bracket that is only moderately tough and does not live for more than one season. (See Fig. 31.) A characteristic feature of this species is the presence along the margin of the fruit body of deep pores which, when the fungus is growing actively, are filled with a clear brown fluid that looks very much like tea.

Treatment and Prevention of Butt Rot

By the time fructifications appear at the base of a tree it is likely that rot is already well established and fairly extensive, and little can then be done to arrest its further spread. Eventually the tree will, almost inevitably, become so weakened that it crashes in some particularly severe gale. However, if the tree is growing fairly vigorously, and the sapwood ring, which receives the greatest stresses, remains alive and sound, the tree may remain standing for a great many years until the decayed heartwood actually disintegrates and disappears, leaving a hollow, but still living, tree. Trees that are growing near buildings or along roads should be felled as soon as fructifications are found growing out from the trunk at, or near, ground level, since it is very difficult to form any opinion as to the extent of the rot from external examination. Similarly, there is little use in keeping infected trees standing if they are being grown for timber. Any increase in girth that they may put on will be discounted by the amount lost as the result of the progressive decay, and the sooner they are felled the better, so as to obtain whatever sound timber remains in them, and to remove a source of infection to other trees in the vicinity.

It is difficult to diagnose the presence of butt rot in the absence of sporophores. In conifers any tendency of the lowest part of the trunk to "barrel" out should arouse suspicion, and of course the presence of decayed roots or of deep unhealed wounds that could provide ports of entry for infection are warnings of possible trouble within.

Only when there is some very special reason, æsthetic or sentimental, for wishing to prolong the life of a tree is it worth while attempting to deal surgically with butt rot.

Prevention of butt rot depends firstly on choosing species of trees that are suited to the land on which they are to be planted; and secondly on avoiding wounds at the base of the tree. Fires should never be lighted near enough to a tree to scorch the bark;

141

there is no surer method of inviting attack by the Honey Fungus. Correct siting of roadside trees when planting will do much to avoid risk of damage by cars parked along the edge of the road. Trees in parks and gardens are often wounded by motor lawn-mowers, and while they are young a ring of bare earth should be kept around them to prevent the groundsman from driving his mower too close. Mechanical extraction of logs by caterpillar-drawn tractors does untold damage to the trees remaining in a stand in which there has been a selective felling. Where deer, goats, or rodents are numerous, the only certain method of protecting young trees is to provide each one with a well-fitting wire-netting guard, set sufficiently far away from it to prevent the animal from reaching the bark.

TOP ROT

So long as the trunk and branches of a tree remain alive and intact fungal infection cannot reach the underlying wood. Prevention of decay on the upper part of a tree therefore depends almost entirely on the avoidance of wounds that expose the wood to infection. Wounds result either from man's careless actions or from natural causes such as storms. High winds may break off the tops and branches of trees at any season, but the most severe damage to broad-leaved trees is done by heavy snowfalls late in the season, when the leaves are on the trees and a far larger amount of snow can therefore be retained on the branches, which often break under the unusual weight. Glazed frosts, in which heavy deposits of ice are formed when the super-cooled rain strikes the twigs and branches, can also cause extensive and devastating damage to all kinds of trees.

Principal Fungi Causing Top Rot

In Conifers. The commonest fungus causing top rot in conifers in America and Europe is *Trametes* (*Fomes*) *pini*. In

142

England it is rare, but is found rather more often on old Pines in the Highlands of Scotland. Its fruit body is a thick, hard, woody bracket, dull coloured on top, with a reddish brown underside in which are much elongated pores. It causes a characteristic decay. (See Fig. 5B.) The wood becomes pitted with small lens-shaped pockets which are lined with a white lint-like material and separated by hard undamaged wood. It is not uncommon to find samples of Douglas Fir imported from America affected in this way. There is no risk

Fig. 32. *Ganoderma applanatum* on Beech.
Fungus gained entry through a branch wound
higher up the trunk.

of this type of rot developing further in sawn timber, nor will it spread to other timber with which it may come in contact.

In Broad-leaved Trees. The commonest fungus causing heart rot in the upper part of the trunk of Beech trees in England is *Ganoderma (Fomes) applanatum.* It forms a thick, hard, broad, woody bracket, smooth, but usually rather lumpy on the top. (See Fig. 32.) The upper surface is a warm brown colour, and usually dusty with the brown spores which are produced in vast numbers. The underside is white when the fungus is growing actively, and the interior, which is very tough, is deep vandyke brown. These fruit bodies can reach a considerable size as they continue to grow year after year. It gains entrance through branch wounds and causes a white flaky rot surrounding a narrow, dark brown invasion zone. Though most common on Beech it is also found on many other trees such as Horse Chestnut, Willow and Elm.

On Elms *Polyporus squamosus* (sometimes known as "the Dryad's Saddle") is the cause of much of the rot in the branches, for which this tree is notorious. Its sporophores are large, stalked brackets, up to a foot across, of a pale creamy colour, but covered on the upper surface with dark-brown scales. The fruit bodies, which appear during the summer, never become woody and towards the end of the year they decompose and fall off. This fungus causes a white flaky rot and sometimes forms tough sheets of pale-coloured mycelium, like wash-leather, filling cracks in the wood. This fungus also occurs on Walnuts and other broad-leaved trees.

On Oaks and Cherries (and incidentally on Yew) the principal cause of heart rot is *Polyporus sulphureus*, the Sulphur Polypore, which is probably the handsomest of all the British polypores. Its fruit bodies, which may reach a huge size and weigh as much as 30-40 lb, consist of overlapping brackets united together at their bases, of a beautiful sulphur yellow colour, edged with a flesh tint. They are soft and fleshy and begin to decompose after a few weeks. This fungus brings about a dry brown crumbling rot which causes the wood to break up into rectangular pieces. Thick sheets of pale-coloured mycelium can often be found filling the cracks in the decayed wood. The fungus can continue to spread in felled timber so long as there is adequate moisture for its growth. Care must therefore be taken when sawing up an Oak log that contains heart rot caused by this fungus to cut away all infected wood. Otherwise the infection may continue to spread and cause early failure when the timber is used as fencing, or in a boat or building.

There are many other fungi that cause top rot in broad-leaved trees. For a more complete list reference should be made to the book by Cartwright and Findlay referred to in the bibliography at the end of this volume.

Prevention of Top Rot in Forests

In forest trees serious decay of the upper part of the trunk usually occurs after they have reached maturity, and have begun to lose large branches, thus opening the way to infection; or when pruning has been carried out injudiciously. (See Fig. 33.) In Great Britain few, if any, stands of over-mature timber remain, and for this reason top rot is of little importance in properly managed woodlands. In the virgin forests of British Columbia, Oregon and Washington, however, heart rot of the trunk is a serious cause of loss in the older stands, and it has been shown that when the trees reach an age of between 250 and 300 years the amount of timber lost by decay equals, and from then on exceeds, the annual increment added by the growth of the trees. Heart rot is also responsible for considerable loss in the utilization of virgin forests in the tropics; the Pencil Cedar in Kenya being an example of a tree that is frequently attacked. Little can be done to mitigate infection in natural forests, but under proper management trees of commercial value will not in the future be allowed to become over-

Fig. 33. Two examples of top rot in Oak. C.C.R. In both cases the infection entered through wounds where a large branch had been removed. In the left hand example the wound healed over after the rot had become established.

mature, but will be felled before heart rot has had time to become serious.

Injudicious pruning can lead to trees becoming infected at quite an early age, and if pruning of broad-leaved trees is undertaken the side branches should be removed cleanly, close to the stem, before they have reached a diameter greater than one to one-and-a-half inches, and certainly before heartwood has begun to form in them. Extensive heart rot has developed in Oaks in parts of the Forest of Dean in trees from which branches three and four inches were cut and the scars left untreated.

In order to obtain from conifers timber that is free from knots, side branches are sometimes removed at an early stage by "brashing", that is, by cleaning the stems completely up to a certain height. If this work is done carelessly with a billhook, wounds may be inflicted that will permit the entry of parasitic fungi. Dead branches may safely be cut off any species of conifer, and quite small live branches (not exceeding an inch in diameter) may, without risk, be removed from Pines, but there is a chance of infection gaining entrance if living branches are removed from Spruce; and on the whole it is wiser to avoid live-pruning of Norway and Sitka Spruce, at least until more is known about the risks involved.

The risk of damage by storms and subsequent infection can generally be reduced by good sylvicultural methods and timely thinning, as these will lead to the production of well-formed trees with balanced crowns and no large side branches. Some damage, however, must almost inevitably be done during a selection felling, when individual trees are felled amongst groups of younger trees that are to be left standing; but this can be greatly reduced by the skilful and careful working of an experienced felling gang. Removal of the stubs of branches broken during felling operations, and the trimming and dressing of the wounds caused by the falling trees, will help to reduce the risk of infection. Mechanical extraction with tractors and winches has greatly increased the amount of damage that occurs during the removal of the felled logs from the woods. While some damage to the spurs and trunks is almost inevitable it can be greatly reduced by careful working, and by the insertion of guards, made from portions of branches, between the steel cables and the trunks of trees round which they may have to pass. Dressing of any wounds inflicted on the standing trees should be considered as part of the general tidying-up operations after felling.

The collection and destruction of the large fruiting bodies of the fungi that cause heart rot has been suggested as a means of reducing the spread of airborne infection in woodland; but probably such measures are seldom worth while, except when an isolated diseased tree is found in an otherwise healthy stand.

Prevention of Top Rot in Park, Roadside and Garden Trees

Though trees are exposed to all kinds of severe weather conditions, care and forethought can do much to mitigate the damage done by gales, heavy snowfalls or thunderstorms. For instance, judicious pruning can lessen the risk of branches breaking off when they are overloaded with snow and ice; weak crotches can be bolted or cabled together; branches that

Fig. 34. Two examples of bad pruning. *Left:* Lime. *Right:* Copper Beech

rub against each other in the wind can be cut off; and exceptionally valuable trees standing in exposed positions can be provided with a conductor to protect them against being struck by lightning.

Careless pruning and the revolting practice of "lopping and topping", often undertaken by unskilled labourers, of so many trees in suburban gardens and streets inflict grievous wounds that lead to infection and heart rot. (See Fig. 34.) As far as possible the removal of large limbs from mature trees should be avoided entirely. Forest trees are out of place in small gardens and in streets, as in a few years they grow so large that they overshadow the houses and gardens, and can then only be kept within bounds by this cruel system of lopping and topping. In such situations it is better from every point of view to plant species of flowering trees that will never exceed a moderate size and require the minimum of pruning.

Unfortunately, owners of property are often too impatient to wait for these slower growing species to develop sufficiently to form a screen, and insist on planting quick growing trees, such as Poplars. These sooner or later will require to be cut back; and of course many gardens already contain large overshadowing trees which simply have to be restrained. In such cases it is often better entirely to remove a few of the larger trees, leaving the smaller ones to develop naturally, rather than to crop them all to a dreadful uniformity of height, leaving a sort of vast hedge in which all the beauty of the individual trees is lost, showing in summer only a mass of greenery, and in winter nothing but some twiggy excrescences at the end of the maimed limbs.

If it is really necessary to reduce the size of a large tree this should be done by the complete removal of some of the larger branches, cutting them off as close as possible to the trunk, and leaving the smaller branches untouched so that the tree still retains a natural outline, and the deplorable maimed look is

149

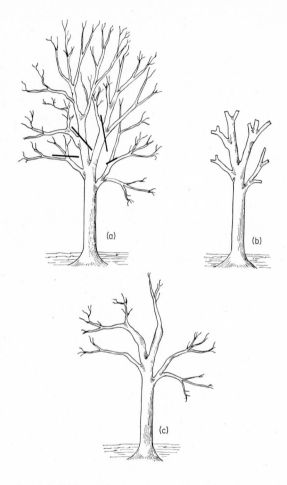

Fig. 35. Right and wrong way of pruning. (a) Tree
to be reduced in size.   Branches should be cut off
as indicated by straight lines. (b) Tree lopped. Shape
permanently ruined.   Wounds   certain   to   become
infected. (c) Tree after pruning, showing minimum
disfigurement.

avoided. (See Fig. 35.) Before cutting off a limb it is always essential first to make an undercut on the lower side so as to prevent the falling limb from tearing the bark away. If the branch is a very heavy one it is best to remove it in two operations. The edge of the wound should always be trimmed as neatly as possible to facilitate healing, and if an irregular area of bark has been torn off the trunk, the wound should be shaped so as to conform with the lines of sap flow, i.e. it should be streamlined in their direction.

Beheading of trees should be avoided whenever possible. Though a few, such as Willow and Poplar, tolerate pollarding, the effect on many others is permanently to ruin their shape, and at the same time to inflict wounds that are unlikely ever to heal and almost certain to become infected. Pollarding of Pines is disastrous as they never again form a proper leader. When conifers are tending to outgrow the space available for them, by far the best way to reduce their size is to remove the lower branches, leaving a tall clear stem with a high crown. Pines, Cypresses and Yews trimmed in this way to form a sort of umbrella can look very beautiful and perfectly natural. If for any reason it is really necessary to behead a tree the cut should always be made at an angle so that the rainwater can run off.

Treatment of Wounds

All but the smallest wounds should receive some antiseptic and protective dressing, so as to reduce the risk of infection and at the same time to prevent the underlying tissues from drying out. The dressing used should be one that will not kill the surrounding bark, or restrict the growth of the healing callus. A great variety of substances have been used for this purpose. At one time Stockholm tar was one of the most popular, but both this and coal-tar creosote have been found to cause injury to the living bark of many species. Mixtures of tar or asphalt (3 parts) with creosote (1 part) are often used; they are cheap

151

and adhere well to fresh cuts, but sometimes cause injury to living tissues. If asphalt alone is used the surface of the cut should first be sterilized with a refined coal-tar oil preservative. When applying tar oils to a sensitive tree such as beech the junction of the wood and the bark where the cambium lies should first be protected with a coat of varnish. Some species of *Prunus, Magnolia* and *Liriodendron* are so sensitive to creosote that it is wiser to use 1/1000 mercuric chloride solution for treating their wounds, following this with a coat of paint or spar varnish. Mercuric chloride is an intensely poisonous substance, and should be handled with great care and only by experienced persons. For the treatment of large transverse cuts a thick layer of bitumen-asbestos mixture has been found satisfactory.

For orchard trees a thick paint made by stirring together raw linseed oil and commercial Bordeaux powder is effective in preventing infection of wounds. The paint should be used soon after mixing; it is poisonous and should not be left within reach of children or animals.

For small wounds not over $1/_2$ in. in diameter on choice trees or shrubs, liquid-grafting wax or spar varnish are probably the safest and easiest substances to apply.

Treatment of Trees Already Infected with Top Rot

In woodlands it is generally best to fell and remove from the woods as quickly as possible all trees that are found to be affected with heart rot, so as to obtain as much sound wood as possible from them and to reduce the risk of infection to the remaining trees.

If trees in parks or gardens are found to be infected, and there is some special reason, such as historical interest or outstanding beauty, why they should be retained, they can sometimes be treated surgically, and this may meet with a fair measure of success, if the decay is localized. Such work should be carried out only by qualified "tree surgeons". In the United States this profession is well organized, and includes many skilful and experienced operators, but in Great Britain, possibly because trees grow more easily and their value for shade is less appreciated, there are only a few qualified practitioners.

The novice should confine his attempts at cavity filling to dealing with minor pockets of decay, as unskilful work may do more harm than good. It is, for example, useless merely to fill up an existing rot cavity with cement as this will shrink away at the edges and allow rainwater to get in. Briefly, the treatment consists in removing all the apparently infected wood, if possible cutting away slightly beyond the discoloured portions and then sterilizing the surface of the exposed wood. An alcoholic solution of mercuric chloride is excellent for this purpose, but, as noted above, it is intensely poisonous and must be handled with extreme caution. The resulting cavity may be left open, but under skilled direction a filling can be inserted over which new growth will be able to spread from the sides. Cement is often used for this purpose but tends to crack in time, and a stiff mixture of sawdust and bitumen or asphalt which remains slightly flexible is more satisfactory.

Bracing and cabling of weak or damaged crotches if carried out skilfully may prevent splitting of the trunk or the loss of heavy limbs, but again this is work that should be carried out only under expert supervision.

Brittleheart

Some trees that grow in the tropics and sub-tropics contain in the heartwood a central core which is much weaker than the rest of the timber in the trunk. This defect, commonly known as brittleheart (or sometimes soft heart or punky heart), affects only a proportion of the trees and is common only in certain species. It occurs most frequently in wood from large over-mature trees such as the African Mahoganies, Gaboon, Idigbo,

Afara, Obeche and Seraya, and in some of the Australian Eucalypts.

The presence of brittleheart in logs can be recognized by the spongy appearance of the wood at the centre. The fibres appear to be broken off short instead of having been cleanly cut and affected wood is usually lighter in weight than sound wood. In sawn timber the defect is not so easily recognized but close inspection of defective material should reveal numerous very fine lines running across the grain (compression failures). Badly affected timber may show actual cross fractures which are known as "thundershakes". If brittleheart is suspected the grain should be tested by raising it with the point of a knife and comparing the break with that obtained in sound wood of the same kind. If brittleheart is present a short "brashy" fracture will result, instead of the longer splintery fracture of sound wood. In fact the effect on the wood is very similar to that of incipient decay except that the colour of the wood is unchanged.

Wood affected with brittleheart has very little strength, and planks containing a high proportion of timber affected in this way will fracture if dropped even a short distance and will sometimes break under their own weight when lifted by one end. Timber suffering from brittleheart should, therefore, obviously never be used for any structural purposes, but there is no risk in using sound timber cut from logs in which brittleheart has been found, as the defect cannot spread. If the sawn hardwood has been graded in the country of origin any brittleheart present should have been eliminated before the timber was shipped.

The cause of brittleheart is still unknown. Careful search has failed to show any evidence that wood-destroying fungi are responsible and it is more probable that the condition is the result of stresses in the growing tree acting on initially rather weak wood. More research is needed, however, to elucidate the cause of this defect, and it will need to be carried out in the countries where the susceptible trees grow. Nothing comparable occurs in the hardwoods grown in the northern temperate zone.

It is of course always possible for trees suffering from brittleheart to become infected with fungi that cause heart rot, and so it may happen that brittleheart is succeeded by heart rot but this is fortuitous, and brittleheart does not necessarily develop into heart rot.

Mistletoe

Occasionally planks will be found to be affected by the suckers of Mistletoe which have penetrated across the grain of the wood like little pencils of intrusive tissue. These may pull out during sawing operations leaving a short fine hole across the grain. In England, Mistletoe is most often found on Apple and Lime trees, but in parts of Europe Silver Fir and Poplar are common hosts, and in some places, notably among the foothills of the Jura, it does serious damage to Firs.

Insect Damage

Standing trees can be attacked by a number of insect pests which may cause damage to the timber of the trunk. Reference to the most important of these has already been made in Chapter 6.

None of the insect pests that attack standing trees is capable of breeding and multiplying in sawn and seasoned timber, though many of them can complete their life cycle in converted timber infested in the fresh green condition.

CHAPTER 9

Care of Timber after Felling and Conversion

As SOON as a tree is felled the natural protection afforded by the bark is largely lost. The green unseasoned wood at the end of the logs is exposed to infection by the airborne spores of fungi and, if the weather is hot, the log may also become the centre of attraction for a variety of insects that infest the bark and underlying tissues. In temperate countries it is customary to fell trees only during the winter months, and in many contracts it is definitely specified that timber shall be winter-felled. Though there is little inherent difference between summer and winter-felled timber there are several good reasons for the practice of restricting felling to the winter, of which the following are the most important.

(1) There is very much less fungal infection in the air during the winter as few fruit bodies of fungi are in active growth during this season. The surfaces of the wood therefore have a chance to dry out before they are exposed to infection.

(2) Owing to the low temperature during the winter months the rate of growth of any fungi that do succeed in infecting the ends of the logs will be very slow.

(3) The ends of the logs dry out gradually and so do not become damaged by the deep splitting and cracking which may develop on logs fully exposed to the hot sunshine and drying winds of summer.

(4) The crown of a deciduous tree is lighter in the winter

than in the summer and so there is less risk of damage to the trunk when it falls.

(5) Game birds in the woods are not disturbed during the nesting season.

(6) Labour required for farm work during the summer may be unoccupied and free to help in felling operations.

(7) In northern countries frost facilitates the work of extraction by consolidating soft ground and muddy tracks.

When dealing with relatively perishable species, such as Beech, it is not sufficient merely to fell the trees in the winter. If loss through decay is to be avoided the logs must also be removed from the woods and sawn up before the warm weather comes. Large quantities of valuable Beech were spoilt during the war owing to delay in converting winter-felled logs. If it is essential to continue sawing Beech throughout the summer it may be better to fell the logs as and when they are required, and to convert them immediately, rather than to fell them all in the winter and hold them in storage throughout the summer. In the tropics, as the temperatures are high throughout the year, there is really no "safe" season for felling. For practical reasons, it may have to be undertaken mainly during the dry season, and the risk of infection is then probably slightly less, though by no means negligible.

Logs only of durable species such as Oak can with safety be left lying on the ground for any length of time during the warmer months. Even with these species loss of the sapwood must be accepted if the logs are not brought out of the woods promptly.

Storage and Protection of Logs

It has been claimed that some kinds of wood improve if left to "season" in the log. While it is just possible that in some timbers certain internal stresses may be relieved during a

157

period of storage in the log, there is little experimental evidence to support this contention. It is true that in stored logs loss of the starch from the sapwood occurs by respiration of the living cells thereby rendering it less susceptible to *Lyctus* attack, but it is doubtful if the advantage thereby gained is worth the risk of decay becoming established in the sapwood. As a general rule it is better to convert logs of most species as soon after felling as possibile.

Whatever the species concerned, all logs should be removed from the woods before the end of the winter and piled on skids in the log yard. Storage yards should be kept free of weeds and undergrowth and of all kinds of rubbish, and no log ends or sapwood offcuts should be allowed to accumulate as these will provide breeding places for *Lyctus* beetles and wood-rotting fungi. All waste wood should be carefully collected and either used as fuel in the sawmill or sold for firewood, for which there is usually a ready market.

The stock of logs should be continuously changing and the logs should be used in the sequence in which they are received; those which have been in storage for any length of time always being used before those that were more recently felled. In spite of the obvious desirability of doing this, it is a common practice in small yards to dump newly arrived logs on top of others that have been felled for some time, and then to work downwards through this pile; and it may well happen that the logs at the bottom remain undisturbed for years, until they eventually rot away. It should always be possible to lay out the storage yard in such a way that logs can be used in proper sequence and that none remains for any great length of time before it is converted.

The best way to store logs of the more perishable species is to keep them submerged under water in a log pond. Since the fungi that cause decay and staining require a certain amount of air for their growth they are unable to develop in wood thus totally submerged. An additional advantage of this method is that there is no risk of the ends of the logs drying out rapidly and splitting. Care should be taken to see that logs stored in water really are completely covered, otherwise the portions that are exposed above the level of the water may deteriorate.

Another method of keeping logs sufficiently saturated with moisture to prevent fungal growth is to expose them to a continuous spray, and this method has been successfully used in Scandinavia for the protection of large piles of logs. It is of course essential that sufficient water should be applied to ensure that the surface of the logs is kept really wet, for as may be easily understood, sprinkling with an insufficient quantity of water only increases the risk of fungal damage by keeping the timber damp. Water storage is ideal for logs of perishable species, such as Birch and Aspen, which are destined for peeling into veneers for the manufacture of plywood, or for matches, as it is in any case desirable to keep these peeler logs in a green condition.

Inspection of Logs and Poles

The most usual indication of unsoundness in logs is the presence of fruiting bodies of fungi on their ends. If fruit bodies are seen on the ends and branch stubs of Beech or Aspen logs it is almost certain that incipient decay will have penetrated several feet. If however the fruit bodies are restricted to a narrow zone of sapwood, as may be the case with Oak logs, then the decay may be entirely confined to this sapwood zone, the heartwood remaining completely sound.

An inspector who has had much practical experience in handling logs of different species will be on the alert to take particular care when he is dealing with the more perishable species such as those listed in Table 1. For example, if Beech logs have been lying in the woods for several months

159

during the warmer half of the year it is very likely that they will have become infected with fungal decay.

Similarly, if one is concerned to discover whether logs have become stained one would be suspicious of Pine logs that had been felled in the spring and left lying around until late summer.

The presence of decay is not always easy to detect in poles that have been barked and piled to air season as infectoin may be concealed within the wood, and the ends of the poles may be dirty and covered with an exudation of resin. It is therefore a good practice to trim off the ends of the poles to permit better inspection before passing them for impregnation. In this way hidden internal decay may be disclosed.

Antiseptic Treatment of Logs

When there are no facilities for under-water storage of susceptible logs the ends, branch stubs, and places where the bark has been scraped off, should be painted with antiseptic immediately (i.e. within twenty-four hours) after the trees are felled. Creosote can be used for this purpose, but if there is any objection to the use of a coloured fluid, a 5 per cent solution of pentachlorophenol in a light oil can be applied. When the period of storage is likely to be prolonged the whole of the log should be sprayed and the treatment may have to be repeated at six-monthly intervals. Under tropical conditions end-treatment is not usually sufficient to give adequate protection, as wood-boring insects are generally active, and these can penetrate the bark and introduce sap-staining fungi. Under European conditions good control of Ambrosia Beetle attack on softwoods has been achieved by spraying the logs with a 0.75 per cent emulsion of gamma BHC.

Where there is a risk of both insect and fungal attack the logs should be completely sprayed with a solution in No. 2 fuel oil of about 2 per cent pentachlorophenol and 0.5 per cent of the gamma-isomer of benzene hexachloride. If insects are not troublesome the latter may be omitted and either a 3 per cent pentachlorophenol solution in oil, or a 3 per cent solution of sodium pentachlorophenate in water can be used alone. The oily solution is preferable to the aqueous if the logs are likely to be floated down rivers, or exposed to heavy rains after treatment, but it is, of course, more expensive. Various proprietary formulations of these antiseptics are available and users will probably find it much more convenient to apply one

Fig. 36. Bad Piling, 1. No proper foundations. Logs blocking airflow under piles of boards. Weeds growing around the timber.

of these, rather than to prepare solutions themselves. A knapsack sprayer of the type used for horticultural purposes can conveniently be used for spraying logs. It is essential that the logs should be turned while they are being treated so as to ensure that the spray shall reach all the surfaces.

These treatments for the control of fungi and insects do

161

not prevent splitting at the ends of the logs. If this is considered likely to occur a special coating containing moisture-resisting ingredients and filler should be applied to the ends of the logs immediately after cutting. There are a number of effective proprietary end coatings on the market, but if anyone wishes to prepare his own the following mixture can be recommended:

Mix thoroughly 10 lb of barytes and 10 lb of fibrous talc (magnesium silicate) into 5 gallons of special gloss oil varnish. The latter, which can be purchased from a varnish manufacturer, is made up of 100 parts rosin, 7 parts hydrated lime and $57\,^1/_2$ parts mineral spirits (all parts by weight). This coating should be applied with a stiff brush, 1 gallon of the mixture being enough to cover about 100 square feet of end surface, i.e. both ends of 30 logs 18 in. in diameter. In order to render this coating fungicidal $^1/_2$ gallon of cresylic acid can be added to 5 gallons of the filled hardened gloss oil. This addition will increase its effectiveness as a protection against the fungi that cause staining and decay.

SEASONING, STORAGE, AND PROTECTION OF SAWN TIMBER

Little or no drying of the timber takes place while it is in the log stage, especially if the bark is left on. This means that freshly sawn timber, even from logs that have been felled for some time, is likely to contain almost as much moisture as it held when the tree was standing. In coniferous sapwood the moisture content is often well over 100 per cent of the oven-dry weight, while hardwoods usually contain 60 to 100 per cent of moisture.

Before timber can be used for any purpose, except rough external work or marine piling, it must be seasoned. As soon as the timber has been sawn up into boards, planks or baulks it should be piled openly so that it can begin to dry out. If timber is left for even a short time in solid piles after it has been sawn it will soon become stained, and if it is left bulk piled for any length of time there is grave risk that it will begin to decay. It is important that the surface layers should be dried off quickly, before airborne infection has a chance to become established. From the point of view of preventing fungal deterioration the more quickly timber is dried the better, but, unfortunately, drying is accompanied by shrinkage, and if the surface layers of the wood are dried too quickly relative to the

Fig. 37. Bad Piling, 2. Note haphazard piling of boards on top of old logs and the profuse vegetation.

core they may crack and check. The rate of drying of the timber must therefore be controlled, and the best time to pile it in the open for air seasoning is during the winter months when the evaporation of moisture from the surface of the wood is slow. Most softwoods and a few hardwoods, however, tolerate rapid drying, and can safely be open piled in late spring or early summer with little risk of excessive splitting.

163

Sawn timber must be piled, very soon after conversion, in such a way that air can circulate freely over all the surfaces of the boards. Except for certain dimension stock such as railway sleepers, fence posts, or furniture squares, which can be cross piled, proper piling-sticks should be used to separate each layer of timber. Generally, softwood sticks 1 in. square in cross-section will be found most satisfactory, but when it is wished to reduce the rate of drying of refractory hardwoods piled in spring or summer then sticks only half an inch thick should be used. It is important that only clean sound sticks should be used for this purpose, as infected or decayed ones may spread their infection to the unseasoned timber with which they come in contact. When not in use, piling-sticks should not be left lying on the ground to pick up infection, but should be stored in a rack. It is a good practice occasionally to dip them in an antiseptic or wood-preservative solution.

Ground on which timber is to be piled for seasoning should be firm and well drained. Grass and other vegetation should first be removed and the surface of the soil then covered with a layer of clinker or ashes. If, at a later stage, weeds become troublesome the ground should be watered with a weed-killer. Sodium chlorate however should never be used in a timber yard as it renders the weeds highly inflammable after they have died and dried off.

Good solid foundations must be provided for the piles. Short brick or concrete columns are best, and the main timbers that rest on these should be thoroughly creosoted. If timber is used for the foundations it must be pressure treated; old railway sleepers are often used for this purpose. It is important that there should be ample ventilation under the piles and there should, therefore, be a clearance of about 18 in. between the bottom layer of timber and the ground. (See Fig. 38.) A gap of one foot should be left between adjacent piles, each of which should be no more than 6 ft wide. Provided that there are

Fig. 38. Correct Piling. Note good foundations so that stack is well off the ground; Piling sticks between each layer of boards properly aligned; roof to keep off rain.

good foundations on firm ground the piles can be made quite high, so long as the boards are carefully stacked and have been sorted so that the longer ones are at the bottom. If the soil is soft, however, or the foundations insecure, the weight of a tall pile may force the foundations to sink and bring the lowest layer timber into contact with the ground. Decaying foundations may lead to irregular sinking of the pile with risk of distorting the timber, and ultimately the whole pile will collapse.

Piles of timber in the open should be provided with some sort of roof to throw off the rainwater, but timber piled to season should never be closely sheeted with tarpaulins. When unseasoned timber is piled in a covered shed it is essential that the sides of the sehd should be sufficiently open to allow a good through current of air. It is far better to pile unseasoned timber in the open than in a badly ventilated shed.

165

It cannot be too often stressed that to reduce the risk of airborne infection and of insect infestation in the seasoning yard it is most important that the whole yard should be kept tidy and free from decaying woody debris and sawdust. All mill waste should be cleared up regularly and burnt, and should never be used to make up roadways and muddy ground.

No trouble with decay in the seasoning piles or stored timber should ever arise in a properly managed yard, but at some times of the year when both the humidity and the temperature are high (as often is the case in this country in the early autumn) moulds and staining fungi may grow on the sapwood of susceptible species and blue stain may develop, even if the timber is quite properly piled. (See Chapter 5.)

In the warmer countries conditions may be favourable for mould growth throughout the greater part of the year and to obtain timber free from stain it may be necessary to take special precautions, such as drying the wood quickly in a timber-drying kiln or by treating it with an antiseptic solution which prevents any fungal growth on the surface. Facilities for kiln drying are not always available in all timber-producing countries, nor does the extra value of the clean timber always warrant the expense of this treatment, which is most economically applied to timber that has already undergone a preliminary air drying.

After a considerable amount of research chemicals have now been found that will, at quite low concentrations, effectively prevent the development of any fungi on newly sawn timber. The most effective of these include the following: the sodium salts of pentachlorophenol and tetrachlorophenol and certain organo-mercury compounds such as ethyl mercury phosphate. Borax at a 5 per cent concentration is reasonably effective on hardwoods. Combinations of these materials have also been used with success and the following is a recommended formula: borax 6 lb, sodium pentachlorophenate 4 lb, water 100 gallons. The exact concentration depends to some extent on local conditions and on the dimensions of the timbers to be treated. In general about 7 lb of sodium pentachlorophenate is required in 100 gallons of water; while about 2 lb in 100 gallons of a compounded organo-mercurial product containing only 6.25 per cent of the active ingredient ethyl mercury phosphate are recommended. The timber must be thoroughly wetted with the antiseptic solution immediately after it has been sawn. If more than twenty-four hours elapse between sawing and treatment the staining organisms may penetrate more deeply into the boards than can the antiseptic solution.

In small mills, where no great quantity of timber ever has to be treated at one time, the boards can be dipped by hand in a trough containing the solution but the operators who do this job should be provided with stout rubber gloves as solutions of highly chlorinated phenols may cause skin irritation. If any appreciable quantity of timber has to be treated it is far more satisfactory to install a mechanically operated dipping vat. The boards are carried on live chains from the saw through a V-shaped trough and over a draining-board from which the fluid that drips off can drain back into the tank. It is only necessary for the boards to remain submerged for a few seconds; all the surfaces must be thoroughly wetted but no deep penetration of the fluid is necessary. No great quantity of the solution, therefore, is used up in any one operation. In one test approximately 15 gallons (U.S.A.) were consumed for each 1000-board feet of lumber treated. After treatment the timber should be piled in the ordinary way to season. Though it is advisable for this to be done as soon as possible, tests have shown that there was surprisingly little deterioration in dipped timber that had been in solid piles for several months.

Precautions for Shipping

If timber of any of the less durable kinds is shipped in an unseasoned condition there is a serious risk that it will deteriorate during a voyage of any length, especially if the ship has to pass through the tropics. Many shipments of timber from the Far East, from South America and from the Pacific coast of North America have arrived in Europe in a mouldy and stained condition with quite a percentage of the pieces suffering also from incipient decay, simply and solely as a result of having been shipped in a wet, unseasoned condition. If timber is properly seasoned before it is exported it seldom suffers any deterioration during a voyage.

If it is necessary in an emergency to ship unseasoned sawn timber it should be dipped, after conversion, in one of the aforementioned antiseptics which will prevent deterioration during the voyage. It must again be emphasized that any dipping treatment which is going to be effective must be given to the timber immediately after it is sawn. It is useless to apply the treatment to timber that has begun to show signs of staining or decay. Although such treatment may prevent further development of moulds and rotting fungi on the surface of the timber, they will continue to grow and cause further deterioration inside the pieces even though these may retain a deceptively clean appearance externally. Once the timber has become infected the best thing to do is to dry it out as quickly as possible either in a kiln or by piling it openly in a well-ventilated place.

Protection of Sawn Timber Against Insect Attack

It is sometimes necessary to protect sawn timber against infestation by wood-boring insects, as well as against fungal infection, and for this dual protection a dip containing 1 to 2 per cent of sodium pentachlorophenate and 1 to 2 per cent of borax together with 5 per cent of "Gammexane" dispersible powder (6.5 per cent gamma BHC), or altenatively one volume of "Gammexane" emulsion concentrate in 70 volumes of fungicidal dip, is recommended. This mixture should be made up as and when required and should be kept stirred during the dipping or spraying operations.

In Australia large quantities of veneers of timbers susceptible to attack by *Lyctus* Powder-post Beetles have been immunized by being steeped in a hot solution of boric acid or borax, and more recently the treatment has also been applied to solid timber. It has been shown at the Forest Products Research Laboratory that even a cold-dipping treatment of green timber in a 5 per cent solution of borax will greatly reduce the risk of infestation in sawn lumber, whether stored out of doors or under cover.

A thorough spraying of timber in early spring with a 2 per cent solution of DDT in miscible oil made up with water will prevent attack during the succeeding summer and possibly for some time longer. "Gammexane" water-dispersible dust applied by spraying a suspension made with 8 oz of the powder in a gallon of water also gives good protection. It is difficult to get any spray thoroughly distributed throughout a pile of timber even if a long spray lance is used, and the results reported of experiments in which the insecticide is applied as a fine mist or fog have not so far been very promising. It is impossible by spraying to reach all the faces of every piece of timber in a stack, and complete protection can be ensured only by dipping each piece in the insecticide before the timber is piled.

As already explained (See page 102), it is possible to sterilize timber that is already infested with beetles by heat, but this treatment does not confer any permanent immunity, and if more lasting resistance to attack is required it is desirable to apply a preservative to kiln-sterilized timber.

Advantages of Kiln Drying as a Means of Preventing Deterioration

If facilities for kiln drying are available, conversion of timber can safely proceed whatever the atmospheric conditions may be and the timber can be dried without any risk of its suffering deterioration as a result of fungal infection or insect attack. It is beyond the scope of this book to describe in any detail the process of kiln drying. In essentials it consists in exposing the timber to controlled conditions of temperature and humidity in a heated chamber. Initially, the humidity of the air is kept up by means of steam sprays, so that the surface of the boards does not dry off too quickly and thereby split or become case-hardened. As the timber dries so the temperature is raised and the humidity gradually lowered until the moisture content of the timber falls to the figure required. The rate at which the drying can proceed depends on the kind of wood and the thickness of the boards. Some hardwoods such as Oak must be dried very slowly but most softwoods can be dried quite rapidly (e.g. in two weeks) without risk of damage. Schedules for various classes of timber have been worked out so that the appropriate treatment can now be given to any species of wood.

Provided that there is a trained operator in charge of the drying kiln who really understands his job most timbers can be kiln dried without serious degrade, and the resultant material should be in better condition than if it had only been air dried. In Northern Europe it is not possible by ordinary air drying to reduce the moisture content of timber below about 18 per cent. If furniture or joinery is made from timber at this moisture content, shrinkage is bound to occur when it is brought into a heated building, in which the equilibrium moisture content will be approximately 12 per cent. Only by kiln drying can the timber be brought to an equivalent moisture content, thereby minimizing the amount of movement that will take place.

There is still a certain amount of prejudice against kiln-dried timber. This no doubt dates back to the time when there was a good deal of ignorance on the subject, and the unskilful operation of kilns led to the production of badly distorted material. It can now be categorically stated that timber that has been properly kiln dried is in no way inferior to the wood that has only been air dried, while for many purposes it is definitely superior. The inherent resistance to fungal decay of kiln-dried wood is just as high as that of wood that has been dried in the open, and, since the moisture content of kiln-dried wood is almost certain to be lower than that of air-dried wood, there is much less risk of its becoming infected with dry rot after it is built into a house than would have been the case had partially dried or unseasoned timber been used.

Recognition of Cause of Damage in Imported Timber

When a cargo of timber is found, on receipt in this country, to be in an unsatisfactory condition a claim against the underwriters may be made on the grounds that deterioration has occurred during the voyage. If the timber can be examined immediately after discharge from the ship a good deal of information as to the cause of the deterioration can usually be obtained. The distribution, amount and nature of the fungal growths should be noted, as well as the depth of any sap-stain or incipient decay that may be present. If decay is found to be at all extensive and to have penetrated more than a fraction of an inch into the boards it is most unlikely to have originated during a voyage of ordinary duration, that is up to six or eight weeks. Similarly deep penetration of sap-stain, which indicates that the sapwood has remained moist for a considerable period, suggests that the timber was shipped in an unseasoned condition. On the other hand, a purely superficial growth of mould, unaccompanied by deep staining, particularly on a species such as Obeche that is very liable to stain suggests that the timber has only been exposed to damp conditions for a comparatively short period.

A number of representative samples should be taken from the parcel and their moisture content determined as soon as possible after removal from the ship. As the end of a plank

171

is often drier than the rest of it, nine inches should be sawn off the end and a full cross-section free from knots and not less than $1/2$ in. thick should be cut. The moisture content of this sample should then be determined by drying it down to a constant weight in an oven maintained between 200° and 220°F. The amount of moisture in a piece of wood is best expressed as a percentage of its oven-dry weight, viz.:

$$\text{Moisture content} = \frac{\text{Initial or wet weight—dry weight}}{\text{dry weight}} \times 100.$$

If therefore a piece of wood loses half its weight after oven drying its moisture content was 100 per cent.

To decide whether a moisture content high enough to be

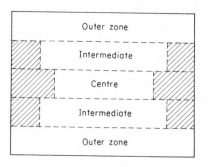

Fig. 39. Method of cutting sample
to determine distribution of moisture.

responsible for staining and deterioration is the result of wetting during a voyage, or whether it was due to original sap being present in unseasoned wood, it is necessary to find out how the moisture is distributed across the section. This can be done by cutting an additional cross-section which is then

172

sub-divided by sawing it up as indicated in Fig. 39. The outer hatched edges are removed from the inner strips before being tested.

If the timber was shipped in an unseasoned condition the moisture content in the centre will almost certainly be higher than in the superficial layers, especially in fairly thick material. If, on the other hand, the moisture of the surfaces is higher than that of the core this is evidence that the timber has been exposed to rewetting after it had been seasoned.

In the experience of the author, when deterioration of timber has occurred during a long voyage it could, in the majority of cases, be attributed to the wood having been shipped in a green, relatively unseasoned condition. Only on very rare occasions could it be attributed to the timber having been wetted by condensation during the voyage.

The term "inherent vice" has been used to describe the innate tendency of a material to deteriorate. This is an unfortunate expression which should never be applied to timber as it suggests that there is some inherent weakness in the wood, whereas in truth damage has occurred as a result of insufficient seasoning or improper storage before shipment.

CHAPTER 10

Decay of Timber in Buildings

FROM the time when men first learned to build themselves dwelling places fashioned out of timber they have had to contend with the problem of fungal decay. There is little doubt that the "leprosy of the house" referred to in Leviticus, Chapter 14, was in fact a fungal infection. Many owners of property in recent years have echoed the words of the prophet, "It seemeth to me there is, as it were, a plague in the house" and have had to follow the old biblical instructions:

" and he shall cause the house to be scraped within round about, and they shall pour out the dust that they scrape off without the city into an unclean place: and they shall take other stones and put them in place of those stones; and he shall take other mortar and plaister the house ".

As soon as men started to build permanent homes they began to take notice of which kinds of wood lasted best in exposed positions, and learned to recognize the varieties that were durable. Even today in parts of Africa one of the quickest ways of finding out which are the most durable kinds of wood is to examine the natives' huts and see which kinds have been used for the centre poles.

In this country there are few references in literature to decay of timber in buildings before the second half of the 18th century, though the rotting of timber in ships had already excited comment. (See Chapter 12.) It is reasonable to suppose that decay became more prevalent after imported softwood had begun to replace the more durable Oak that hitherto had been so widely used in our buildings. Towards the end of the 18th century the trouble had evidently become widespread and serious for the Royal Society of Arts offered, in 1784, a premium or prize in the form of a gold medal "for the discovery of the various causes of the dry rot in timber and the certain method of prevention". This prize was duly awarded some ten years later to a Mr. Batson, who had effectively treated an outbreak six years previously by removing all the earth under the floor and replacing it with "anchor-smiths' ashes". The Transactions of this Society during the succeeding twenty years contain a number of interesting references to this subject, and James Randall, writing in 1807, described it as one of "considerable importance on account of the devastation produced in some of the finest buildings in the country" and referred to the fact that the great dome of the Bank of England as originally built by Sir Robert Taylor was destroyed by this same rot.

Dry rot became prevalent after the First World War when large quantities of unseasoned timber were used and new methods of construction were employed; but it was only during, and after, the Second World War that it became really widespread, and so common in some districts as to cause alarm. There were some streets in London in which every house had had it in varying degree, and in some of the larger country mansions damage amounting to tens of thousands of pounds was caused by dry rot. One expert estimated that repairs to buildings affected by rot cost the country a total of about £ 20 million annually for many years after the war ended. The reason for this increase was the general neglect of ordinary maintainance during the war years, coupled with the damage caused by the bombing, and the fact that for many years many buildings were left empty, especially in the coastal areas.

The term "dry rot", now so widely applied to the decay of timber in buildings, appears first to have been used about 1765. It is, as Benjamin Johnson rightly said in 1803, a misnomer to call this decay "dry" rot as it is invariably encouraged by dampness. The term doubtless originated from the fact that wood in the final stages of decay cracks up and falls to a dry powder when handled. There is no precise definition of what is meant by dry rot, the term being used loosely to describe any brown, crumbling rot of timber in buildings. Strictly speaking the name should be confined to the decay brought about by fungi with water-conducting strands; and in Great Britain by the true Dry Rot Fungus, *Merulius lacrymans*, and throughout this chapter it will be thus applied. There are occasions when a legal definition of what is meant by dry rot may become important, as for instance when the terms of a repairing lease specifically exclude repairs due to dry rot, or when a property is sold on the express understanding that it is free from dry rot. The definition of the term given in a British Standards list of terms reads as follows: "A general term applied to the decay of timber caused by the attack of certain fungi (especially *Merulius lacrymans* in Great Britain) as a result of which the wood becomes light in weight and friable".

The fungi that cause decay in buildings may be divided into two groups:

(1) Those that grow in external woodwork such as wooden sills, roof shingles, and wooden siding or cladding, where the conditions are similar to those to which other woodwork in the open is exposed; as for instance, (a) alternate wetting and drying (though the presence of a well maintained paint film will reduce these fluctuations in moisture), and (b) extremes of temperature. One therefore tends to find in these places fungi, such as species of *Lenzites*, that can tolerate being dried up for quite long periods, and will then revive on rewetting—in

fact a similar range of species to those that cause decay in fencing.

(2) The other group consists of a few "house" fungi which are adapted to the rather specialized conditions that exist in buildings. Nearly all the serious damage is caused by a few species. In Europe the Dry Rot Fungus, *Merulius lacrymans*, and the Cellar Fungus, *Coniophora cerebella*, are outstandingly the most prevalent. Between them they have probably been responsible for over 95 per cent of all the damage that has occurred. In America *Poria incrassata* is probably the most important of the fungi with water-conducting strands that infect buildings. It resembles *Merulius lacrymans* in its way of growth and its mode of attack.

Fungi that Cause Decay in Exposed Woodwork

It is comparatively rare to find fully developed fructifications of wood-rotting fungi on the external woodwork of buildings and so the identity of the fungus present is not always obvious. However, since the remedial treatment required does not vary greatly according to the species of fungus that has been responsible for the rot, it is not essential for practical purposes to diagnose the precise cause.

In England *Polystictus versicolor* is one of the commonest causes of decay in hardwood sills in which it causes a spongy white rot. This fungus is a thin, tough polypore with a fine white pore surface on the underside and a hairy upper surface zoned with shades of grey and rusty red.

Poria contigua is another fungus that is occasionally found on window sills and frames, causing a very stringy white rot in hardwoods and softwoods. It often forms tufts of tawny brown mycelium around the sporophores and in cracks in the decayed wood. It is said to be one of the major causes of decay of timber in buildings in New Zealand.

Lenzites sepiaria, a dark brown gill fungus with a tough, woody texture, is probably one of the commonest fungi on wooden buildings in the Alpine regions of Europe, and it has been reported to be very common on buildings in Eastern America. It is very resistant to desiccation and can retain its vitality after years of storage under dry conditions. It causes a brown cubical rot.

Lenzites trabea is similar to *Lenzites sepiaria* but paler in colour. In the warmer parts of Europe and America it is an important cause of decay of timber in buildings, particularly in wooden roofs that suffer condensation. It is more resistant to arsenical wood preservatives than most wood-rotting fungi and produces a garlic-like odour when growing on wood containing traces of arsenic.

Fungi That Cause Decay in Buildings

Dry Rot Fungus—*Merulius lacrymans*

So far as is known *Merulius lacrymans* has never been found in England growing in a wild state on fallen timber in the forest. It has, however, been reported on good authority, to occur on Spruce logs in the temperate regions of the Himalayas at an altitude of 8000-10,000 feet, and this may well have been its original home. It is sometimes found, though not very commonly, on pitwood in mines. It requires for its growth rather constant conditions of temperature and humidity and, like some greenhouse plants, is intolerant of draughts. The alternations of heat and cold, sunshine and rain, to which woodwork in the open is exposed are fatal to its growth, and so it is never found on fencing, railway sleepers or poles. It thrives best in humid, unventilated places where the air is quite still and the woodwork is damp but not saturated. Under such conditions, which may exist in an unventilated cellar, the fungus will form thick luxuriant masses of white mycelium, that look like snowdrifts. On the surface of this mycelium there sometimes appear glistening drops of liquid which are secreted by the fungus and from which it derives its name of *lacrymans* or "weeping". *Merulius* is able, by its chemical action on the wood substance, actually to synthesize water, and this weeping habit is the means by which the fungus can discharge water of metabolism that might under still, humid conditions render the wood too moist for its further development. Usually the mycelium soon develops tinges of pinkish lilac and here and there patches of bright lemon yellow. Under less humid conditions the fungus forms sheets of silvery-grey mycelium which have a somewhat silky texture when torn, owing to the hyphæ growing parallel to each other. (See Fig. 40.)

A striking characteristic of this fungus is its ability to form strands which are sometimes as thick as a pencil. These strands, which contain specialized wide hyphæ that function like the vessels in wood, enable the fungus to transport water from the damp place in which it first established itself to the ever extending margin of its growth, thus enabling it to attack nearby relatively dry wood. These strands can easily penetrate through plaster, masonry and brickwork and can travel for distances of many yards over, or through, inert materials from which the fungus is unable to draw any nourishment. (See Fig. 45.) The strands generally work their way through the mortar joints in brickwork, but are occasionally found actually inside unbroken bricks if these are fissured. These strands on drying become brittle and can be snapped across between the fingers. It is this ability to penetrate through brickwork and masonry which makes *Merulius* such a dangerous pest and one so difficult to eradicate.

After the fungus has been growing in woodwork for perhaps two years or more it usually forms its fruit bodies which, on horizontal surfaces, are shaped like pancakes, but, on a vertical

179

A small fruit body is the only indication of rot.

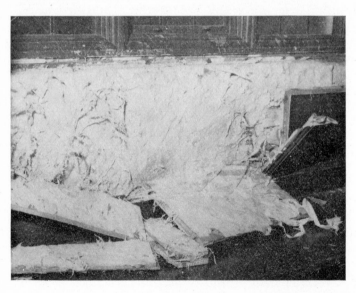
Extent of the fungus growth revealed when the panel
was pulled down.
Fig. 40. Dry rot in wooden window seat. C.C.R.

Fig. 41. Dry rot in window lining. Note the cross cracking of the decayed wood and the deposit of spores on the cobwebs. C.C.R.

surface, often take the shape of thick brackets. They appear at almost any time of year but develop most abundantly during the "mushroom season", that is, towards the end of the summer. They are tough in texture and have a wrinkled surface something like tripe. Their colour is at first grey with tinges of lilac, but as the rusty red spores develop the whole fruit body, with the exception of a narrow margin that

181

o

Fig. 42. Dry rot in flooring and cupboards in a ground floor
room that had been rendered gas-proof during the war. Note
masses of mycelium and the cross cracking on under side of
floor boards.

remains greyish white, acquires a rich rusty-red colour. The
spores are produced in fantastically large numbers; it has been
estimated that a fruit body a yard across can give off fifty
million spores a minute for days on end. In a room where
there are several large fruit bodies of *Merulius* everything may
become covered with a thick deposit of these spores looking
like red dust. The spores often drift in the air for quite a
distance and may even come up through cracks between floor
boards, so that the powder appears in other rooms where there
are no fungal growths, often puzzling an unwitting housewife
who wonders why she has to dust away this reddish powder

182

so often. Under the microscope these spores, which measure about 10 microns (1/100 mm) in length, appear as rather thick-walled, golden yellow, oval bodies.

The fruit bodies of the Dry Rot Fungus develop on the surface of skirtings, door- and window-frames, etc., as well as on plaster and brickwork, and sometimes, in a heavily infected building, they even appear on the outside of the walls, and they are frequently the first indication that rot exists in a building. (See Fig. 44.) They dry up or decompose after a few weeks and are often consumed by insects. If the fungus is

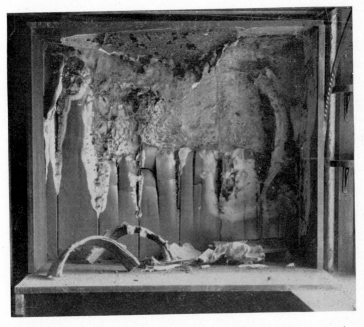

Fig. 43. Dry rot in match boarding in a cupboard. Note warping of boards towards the most severely decayed side and fruit bodies of *Merulius lacrymans* at the top.

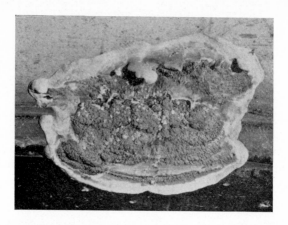

Fig. 44. Fruit body of *Merulius lacrymans*, Dry Rot
Fungus, on skirting.

left undisturbed fresh crops of fruiting bodies may be produced
each year, until the fungus has exhausted all the nourishment
in the wood.

Wood decayed by this fungus has a characteristic appearance; it is pale brown in colour, and falls to powder when crum-
bled between the fingers. On drying it shrinks considerably
and breaks up into rather large brick-shaped pieces, with deep
cracks along and across the grain. (See Fig. 41.) If panelling and
skirting boards are attacked, the side of the woodwork next to
the wall is usually more severely decayed than the exposed face.
It therefore shrinks more on drying and the boards tend to
warp. (See Fig. 43.) The dry rot hidden behind is thus revealed
at last by the collapse of the surface of the affected woodwork
due to this shrinkage and warping.

Merulius can decompose many different kinds of wood,
including some relatively durable species such as oak and
mahogany, but it usually spreads to these latter only after it
has established itself on a softwood.

184

Cellar Fungus—Coniophora cerebella

Coniophora cerebella is a very common fungus and, unlike *Merulius lacrymans,* is often found on decaying timber lying on the ground in the open. There is, therefore, always a chance that perfectly sound timber may be carrying the spores of this fungus when it is built into a house, but these will only germinate and set up rot if the timber is thoroughly wetted.

Fig. 45. Strands of *Merulius lacrymans* on brickwork.

185

Coniophora requires even moister conditions for its development than does *Merulius,* and the decay which it causes is often referred to as "wet rot". It never forms superficial masses of mycelium, the most it produces being a thin, yellowish brown skin. Its strands soon become dark brown in colour (See Fig. 46B.); they are never thicker than stout twine and they do

Fig. 46. Cellar Fungus, *Coniophora cerebella.* C.C.R.
A. Wet rot. Typical decay showing longitudinal cracking more pronounced than transverse cracking.

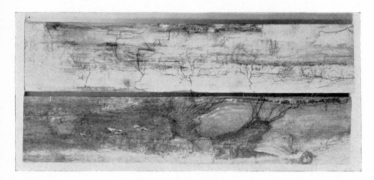

Fig. 46. B. Strands of the fungus on floor boards.

Fig. 47. Wet rot. Internal decay caused by *Coniophora cerebella*.
C.C.R.

not penetrate into brickwork, though they occasionally spread
over the surface of damp plaster forming dark, fern-like growths.
The fruit body is an inconspicuous skin bearing little pimples
or rounded lumps on which the spores are produced. (See
Fig. 48.) When quite fresh it is olive-green in colour but soon
darkens to an olive-brown. Under high magnification the
spores appear a pale olive-brown and are about the same length
as those of *Merulius* but plumper. They are never produced
in such quantities as to become obvious to the naked yee.

Coniophora, which attacks both hard and soft woods, causes
the wood in which it is growing to crack up, but the individual
pieces into which it breaks are generally smaller than those in
wood rotted by *Merulius*, and most of the cracks run along the
grain. (See Fig. 46.) In freshly attacked wood there is often

187

a line of yellow staining at the edge of the decayed portion. It is not uncommon to find decay caused by this fungus confined to the interior of a board or joist, with a superficial layer of pratically sound wood concealing the internal rot. (See Fig. 47.) The severely decayed wood often becomes very dark or almost black in colour. Under very damp conditions *Coniophora* can cause severe and rapid decay, but the fungus *does not extend beyond the area which is damp* and cannot therefore cause such widespread havoc as can *Merulius*.

Fig. 48. Fruit body of *Coniophora cerebella* on log.
C.C.R.

Pore Fungi

There are several species of Poria that sometimes occur in buildings. All these fungi have thin, flat fructifications, usually white in colour, on the surface of which are numerous small round holes, or pores, on the walls of which the spores are borne.

Poria incrassata. The "Building Poria" is the American counterpart of *Merulius lacrymans* to which it must be closely related, and the decay which it causes is almost indistinguishable from that caused by *Merulius*. It is outstandingly the most important destroyer of coniferous timber in the United States, particularly near the Southern and Pacific coasts. It produces branching, water-conducting strands, and sheets and felts of mycelium. The annual leathery, crust-like fruit bodies vary in colour from orange to olivaceous, according to their age.

Poria vaillantii. This Poria is probably the commonest species in Europe. It brings about a rather similar decay in softwoods to *Merulius* but its mycelium, fruit bodies, and strands always remain white or nearly white, and its strands, which never reach the size of the larger *Merulius* strands, remain flexible when they dry. Under very humid conditions in mines this fungus may produce great white tassels of mycelium. (See Fig. 51.) *Poria vaillantii* can cause severe damage locally in a building, but it has only limited powers of extending beyond the damp area in which it has become established, and so is less dangerous than *Poria incrassata* or *Merulius lacrymans*.

Lentinus lepideus—Stag's Horn Fungus

This is an Agaric which in the open has a typical toadstool type of fruit body, with a pale brown, scaly cap, and a tough, almost woody consistency; but in buildings and mines where there is little or no light its fructifications fail to develop properly and consist of rounded, much branched stalks, reminiscent of antlers. (See Fig. 49.) The whitish mycelium shows purplish brown spots. It causes a brown cubical rot in softwoods, and

189

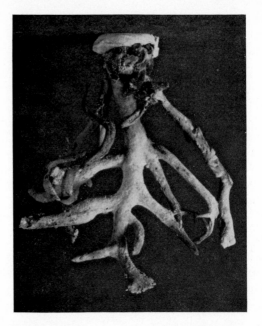

Fig. 49. Abortive sporophores of *Lentinus lepi-deus*, Stag's Horn Fungus, found under a floor.

imparts to the decayed wood a characteristic sweet, aromatic smell, resembling that of balsam. It is a common cause of decay in poorly creosoted sleepers and poles, having a certain degree of resistance to low concentrations of tar oils. In buildings it sometimes occurs where there has been persistent leakage of water and can be regarded as a form of wet rot.

Paxillus panuoides

This fungus, which has no popular name, is an Agaric with a soft, fleshy, fan-shaped fruit body, almost stalkless, the upper surface a dingy yellow, and the gills ochre brown. (See Fig. 50.) It causes a brown crumbling rot in softwoods, and imparts

190

a reddish brown tinge to the decayed wood. The fine, branching, yellowish strands do not darken like those of *Coniophora*. It requires very moist conditions for its growth and causes only localized decay.

Phellinus megaloporus (formerly called *Phellinus cryptarum*)

This fungus, which at one time was thought to be very rare, has been found in a number of old buildings in this country, causing decay in large oak timbers. It is reported to have been

Fig. 50. Young fruiting bodies of *Paxillus panuoides*.

responsible for serious damage in the Palace of Versailles. The fruit body, which is usually shaped like a short thick bracket, is tough and woody, dull fawn or biscuit coloured, with a pore layer, sometimes several layers thick, of a similar colour. It brings about a white, fibrous, stringy rot, and wood decayed by this fungus is readily attacked by Death-Watch Beetles.

Fungi that Occur in Houses but are Harmless to Woodwork

Under very damp conditions certain fungi may appear on

191

TABLE 5. *Principal fungi in buildings*

Fungus	Fruit Bodies	Strands	Growths on Wood	Effect on Wood
Merulius lacrymans	Fleshy, rather tough. Shaped like pancake or bracket. Spore surface wrinkled into pores; rusty red colour, edge grey.	Plentiful, greyish; may be as thick as a pencil; often in brickwork; brittle when dry.	Soft masses like cotton wool in humid places; otherwise grey silky skins with lilac and yellow tinges.	Rotted wood breaks up into brick-shaped pieces, pale brown colour.
Poria vaillantii and other white species of *Poria.*	Soft, whitish plates covered with minute pores.	Whitish; never thicker than stout twine; flexible when dry.	Whitish, cottony sheets. No bright colours appear.	Rotted wood breaks up into brick-shaped pieces, pale brown colour.
Coniophora cerebella.	Thin; olive green or olive brown, bearing warts.	Dark brown, branching. Sometimes spreading over but never penetrating bricks or stone.	Only thin skin; yellowish when fresh, soon darkening.	Rot sometimes entirely internal leaving a sound skin of wood. Decayed wood usually darkened and much split along the grain.
Lentinus lepideus	Perfect form is a tough toadstool. In buildings usually tough, branched, rounded antler-like stalks.	None	Whitish skin with purplish brown patches.	Rotted wood goes brown and crumbles, has sweet, aromatic smell.
Phellinus megaloporus (P. cryptarum)	Hard, tough bracket or stratified pore layer; fawn colour.	None	Thick, matted, fawn-coloured sheets.	White, stringy rot in Oak. Often followed by beetle attack.

192

the plaster or brickwork which are quite harmless to the timber. Of these, Elf Cups (*Peziza* sp.) are perhaps the commonest. They are little, soft, yellowish brown cups about an inch across, and a crop of them sometimes appears on a ceiling that has been soaked by flooding. They shrivel up when dry and almost disappear.

Species of Inky Cap (*Coprinus* sp.), which are delicate, soft toadstools that dissolve into an inky fluid when mature, often grow on damp cellar walls, and sometimes appear between flagstones laid on the earth.

Although these fungi do not themselves cause decay in woodwork their appearance is a warning that dangerously damp conditions, favourable for an outbreak of dry rot, exist and should at once be remedied.

DETECTION OF DRY ROT

Since the cost of repairing decayed woodwork may be very considerable if dry rot is allowed to proceed unchecked, it is highly desirable that an outbreak should be detected and dealt with before it has had a chance to become extensive. Under favourable conditions the fungus can spread very rapidly, and it is not uncommon to find the floor of a fair-sized room decayed to the point of collapse within two years of infection becoming established.

When surveying a house with a view to purchase it is important that the existence, nature and extent of any decay or insect damage that may be in the woodwork should be discovered, so that the cost of repairing the damage may be roughly assessed. Many instances could be quoted of unwary puchasers buying houses infected with dry rot, repairs for which subsequently cost hundreds, or even thousands, of pounds. On the other hand, most older houses contain odd patches of wet rot, or traces of woodworm attack, which can often be dealt with at a trifling cost, so that a surveyor should be able not only to discover such defects, but also to assess their significance and the probable cost of putting them right. In fact he must be able to steer a middle course between the risk of letting his client in for future trouble and the risk of alarming him unduly and frightening him off buying a quite sound property because he has found an "odd spot of rot".

While patches of wet rot may be found in buildings of any age or type, true dry rot is, in the author's experience, most likely to be found in:

Large country mansions with parapet gutters, complicated roofs, and badly designed rainwater disposal systems; city and town houses built between (approximately) 1750 and 1930;

Housing estates built between 1920 and 1930 on low-lying badly-drained land;

Buildings that have stood empty for years or which suffered damage during air raids or in which fires have occurred.

Dry rot is more prevalent in some parts of the country than in others. In general it is more likely to be common in the low-lying and the wetter, more humid areas. Parts of London, the Thames valley, Merseyside, North and South Wales, Glasgow, the West coasts of Scotland and Ireland are districts in which dry rot has been particularly troublesome. In America the areas in which the Building Poria has caused most damage are the Gulf States and the Pacific North West. However, despite these generalizations no part of the country and no type of building can be considered as entirely immune, though *Merulius lacrymans* is seldom found in all-timber buildings or in really old cottages and farmhouses in which the timbers are mainly of Oak.

The symptoms to be looked for when a building is being examined for signs of decay are:

Signs of damp due to overflowing gutters and leaking down

pipes. If such damp is discovered, nearby woodwork should be examined.

A mushroomy or "fungussy" odour. Thes mell of *Merulius* is distinct, and once smelt is never forgotten; but a musty or mouldy smell must not be considered as conclusive proof that there is dry rot in a house.

Any warping or collapse in the surface of skirting, archi-traves, door or window linings, or matchboarding.

Dropping of floor boards due to decay in joists or wall plates.

Rusty red spore powder, more likely to be found in little-used places, such as basements, than in living-rooms.

Any suspicious pieces of wood should be tested with a fine bradawl, a bodkin, or a penknife. If the wood is sound it will resist the entry of the tool and the fibres will grip the point. If decayed the probe can be inserted and withdrawn easily. The parts of a house in which dry rot is most likely to be found are basements, bathrooms, kitchens, lavatories and wash-houses. Roofing timbers are attacked only if there has been persistent leakage; in older buildings parapet gutters are a frequent source of trouble.

ERADICATION AND CURE OF DRY ROT

When decayed timber is discovered in a building the first step is to find out which fungus has been responsible. If *Merulius* is found to be the culprit the procedure should be:

A thorough and careful survey must be made to find out how far the fungus has spread. Floor boards must be taken up and hidden woodwork exposed so far as may be necessary to trace the full extent of the outbreak.

Timber that shows any signs of decay or on which there are fungal growths must then be cut away. The cuts should be made 18 in. or so beyond the last signs of attack, as the infection may be present inside the wood beyond the visible indications on the surface. Care should be taken to remove any decayed timber embedded in the walls, such as fixing plugs or battens, bond timbers, and lintels. The decayed timber should at once be taken from the building and burnt on the site. It should never be sold to a firewood merchant, as infection might thereby be spread to many other buildings.

Plaster found to be permeated with fungus strands should be stripped from the walls to a distance a little beyond the last trace of the fungus.

Any brickwork or masonry with which the decayed wood has been in contact is likely to contain strands of the fungus, and these may have penetrated throughout its thickness. An effort must therefore be made to sterilize it or at least to treat it so that growths of fungus shall not later emerge to infect the new timber; but to do this is no easy matter. The method usually adopted is to brush down the wall, and rake out any loose mortar from the joints in the brickwork, after which the flame of a powerful blow-lamp, or flame-gun, is played slowly over the brickwork until its surface is too hot to touch. When carrying out this treatment it is a good plan to mark out the wall into square yards, and to instruct the workmen to play the flame over each unit for a definite period, about ten minutes, or a little more or less according to the thickness of the brickwork and how wet it is.

This treatment, however, cannot be guaranteed to kill all fungus throughout the thickness of a 14-18 in. wall. It is therefore necessary also to apply an antiseptic in such a way as to form a "*cordon sanitaire*", and this should poison any growths emerging from strands that may be left alive in the depths of the wall. A number of chemicals have been successfully used for this purpose. Substances that may damage mortar, such as strong acids, or which might interfere with subsequent redecoration, such as tar oils, must be avoided. Aqueous

196

solutions of salts that are toxic to fungi are generally used. Sodium pentachlorophenate at 5 per cent concentration (about 8 oz to the gallon of water) has largely replaced the chemicals formerly used and has been found to be most effective. Sodium orthophenylphenate at a similar concentration has also been used successfully for sterilizing brickwork infected with *Merulius*. This solution is less of an irritant than that of sodium pentachlorophenate and for this reason may be preferred if it has to be applied by spraying. There are a number of proprietary products on the market suitable for application to infected brickwork which contain these chemicals.

If the source of dampness responsible for the outbreak of rot can be traced and dealt with, and the infected wall can be dried out and kept dry, then the surface sterilization described above is usually entirely effective—provided, of course, that it has been carried out thoroughly and conscientiously. If however, for any reason, the dampness in the walls cannot be effectively cured more elaborate measures are necessary. If the masonry or brickwork is in a poor state and severely infected the safest course is to pull the wall down and rebuild it; but there are many cases in which the infection can be dealt with quite satisfactorily by an "irrigation" treatment. Holes, half an inch in diameter, are drilled into the wall, sloping slightly downwards to a depth of 6-9 in. at 18 in. centres at the upper limit of the infection. The solution is poured into these holes until it soaks down inside the wall and appears at similar holes cut at the bottom of the infected area. This treatment requires skilful handling and is best undertaken only by experienced operatives. After impregnation the wall must be allowed to dry out before redecoration is attempted as soluble salts may come to the surface and crystallize out as a white powdery efflorescence.

Another method, which has given very promising results, is to coat the surface of the brickwork, after the heat treatment,

197

P

with an antiseptic plaster, or rendering, based on zinc oxychloride cement. The advantage of this method over the irrigation treatment is that it avoids the introduction of large quantities of salts into the wall, thus reducing the risk of damage to any decorative finish that is applied later.

Existing sound woodwork that has been exposed during eradication work should be sprayed or brushed, twice, with an effective wood preservative.

All new timber to be used in repairs should be thoroughly treated with wood preservative. If dampness is likely to persist the new structural timbers should be steeped in a bath of preservative for several days, or else impregnated under pressure. If, however, generally dry conditions can be established without undue delay, surface treatment by three brushed-on coats should give adequate protection. Concrete lintels should be used in place of wooden ones that have decayed. Bonding timbers should never be replaced, and the cavities left after their removal should be bricked up. Fixing plugs should be replaced by nailable concrete or breeze. Unnecessary, purely ornamental woodwork should not be replaced unless it has real artistic value. Window-boards and linings can be replaced by plaster applied directly to the brickwork. New skirtings can often with advantage be run in cement.

Lastly, but perhaps the most important step of all, the source of dampness originally responsible for the outbreak must be sought and corrected.

Treatment of Dry Rot in Valuable Woodwork

If dry rot is found to have attacked the back of valuable antique panelling, or carved wooden decorations, without destroying their outward appearance, such woodwork can usually be saved. The panelling should be very carefully taken down and laid on a flat surface, or stood upright against a straight wall, with the decayed side exposed to the air. When it is quite dry any fungus growths and badly softened wood should be gently scraped off, or brushed away with a wire brush, and the wood should then be given three flowing brush treatments with a solvent type preservative, at intervals of at least one day between each treatment. As much of the preservative as possible should be allowed to soak into the wood. After the preservative has dried off it may be found desirable to strengthen badly decayed portions by screwing light battens of treated wood on to the back of the panelling before refixing it on the wall. Ventilation should be provided to the back of such treated panelling when it is refixed. If the preservative treatment is thoroughly done and further access of moisture prevented, there should be no risk of the Dry Rot Fungus again becoming active or of the rot extending any further.

If the laths in a decorated or painted ceiling are found to be infected it may be possible, if the ceiling can be supported from beneath, to repair it without taking it down. The decayed laths must be picked out and fine-gauge wire netting screwed to the ceiling joists should be fixed with fresh plaster on to the old ceiling. The new plaster must be of a kind that will marry successfully with the old. This type of work requires highly skilled supervision and specialist advice should be sought in any important case.

Treatment in situ

When dry rot is found to have attacked the end of a principal beam, or a main roof truss, the removal of which would involve great expense, it can, in some cases, be treated *in situ*. This treatment can be attempted with a fair prospect of success provided that (*a*) the rot has not penetrated deeply, (*b*) the end can be fully exposed, and (*c*) further access of moisture can be prevented. The procedure in such cases is as follows:

After exposing the end of the beam, any softened wood on the surface should be removed with a chisel or adze. If, on drilling into it, the beam is found to be decayed internally the end should be cut off a little way beyond the last signs of attack, and a new end of treated timber bolted on, with iron or steel plates on each side. If, on the other hand, the beam is found to be internally sound a series of $1/2$ in. or $3/4$ in. holes should be bored to two-thirds the depth of the beam into the upper surface, at intervals in three staggered rows across the end of the beam. These holes should then be repeatedly filled, through a funnel, with a solvent type preservative which will seep into the wood and form a barrier to any fungus attempting to grow along it. When replacing the brickwork the sides and top of the beam should be left exposed for inspection, so that any fresh development can at once be spotted and dealt with.

Treatment of Wet Rot

When woodwork is found to be decayed but no traces of fungi with water-conducting strands, such as *Merulius lacrymans*, can be found, the condition is usually referred to as "wet rot". None of the fungi responsible for this type of rot spreads much beyond the area that has been damp, nor do they form strands which penetrate into brickwork, and therefore less drastic treatment will suffice. Wood that is actually decayed must, of course, be cut out, and it should be replaced with timber that has been thoroughly treated with a preservative. The source of dampness must be sought and checked, and the ventilation beneath any suspended floors that are affected should be improved by the insertion of additional air vents in the walls. Where wet rot has been caused by direct leakage it can often be entirely checked by removing the source of moisture and by thorough and rapid drying. There is little risk of any recrudescence of wet rot even if small traces of infection are left, provided that no further access of moisture occurs, but decayed wood is attractive to wood-boring insects, and for this reason alone it is undesirable that any appreciable quantity should be left in position. Great care should be taken to remove all decayed wood from any part of a building in which dampness is likely to persist.

PRINCIPAL CAUSES OF DAMP IN BUILDINGS

It has been already explained that dry rot can develop only if moisture reaches the woodwork in sufficient amounts to raise and keep its moisture content to over 20 per cent for an appreciable period, at the least for some months. It is therefore obvious that whenever dry rot is found there must have been some source of damp, but sometimes quite a lot of detective work is required to discover this, especially if the building has recently been redecorated. In cases where there is absolutely no evidence of damp penetration, nor any record of flooding since the building was erected, it may be that the moisture was in the timber itself when it was put into the building, i.e. that the wood was unseasoned.

The three main sources of damp in buildings are:

Through, or up, the walls.
Leakage from plumbing or from rain water pipes.
Condensation, either of moisture rising from the ground beneath the building, or of moisture from operations carried on inside, such as washing or cooking.

Walls

Direct penetration of moisture through solid walls occurs when these are built of solid stone or brick, or when the mortar has perished. It can be reduced by rendering the wall externally, but the surest protection is to have a cavity wall.

Defective guttering and cracked and leaking rainwater pipes are frequently the cause of severe local dampness. It would be no exaggeration to say that at least 75 per cent of the outbreaks of dry rot in recent years have been due to neglect of maintenance of the rainwater disposal system. Down pipes set close against the wall cannot be painted at the back and eventually rust and corrode away. Pipes that become blocked remain full of water which freezes in cold weather, resulting in cracks. Very often down pipes become hidden from view by an overgrowth of creepers, so that leakage goes on for years before it is detected. (See Fig. 51.)

Brick and stone are both slightly porous materials; therefore if the foundations of brick or stone walls are set on damp soil moisture will rise in them by capillary attraction unless an impervious layer, or damp-proof course, is inserted in the wall

Fig. 51. Gutter blocked with leaves and vegetation — a frequent cause of dry rot.
C.C.R.

above the soil level. Damp-proof courses may be made of slates, lead, bitumen, or of several courses of "blue" bricks. If there are flower beds around a house the level of the soil will tend to rise every time manure, etc. is applied. If the soil level is allowed to rise above the damp-proof course the base of the wall will soon become damp.

Plumbing Leakages

Leakages from plumbing are generally obvious and are therefore remedied without delay; but sometimes pipes that are embedded in brickwork corrode away, or a pipe below floor level springs a pin leak, and slow leakage goes on for years before it is discovered. During the war, when so many houses were left unoccupied, or were only occupied at irregular intervals, many cases of flooding occurred as a result of burst pipes during frosty weather, and many severe outbreaks of dry rot developed in consequence. If a house is to be left empty during frosty weather the whole water system should be drained.

Condensation

In many of the older houses the ground beneath the floors is bare earth, and this remains permanently damp if the soil is a heavy clay or the site is a low-lying one. The moisture evaporates continuously and may condense in the floor boards, thus rendering them damp enough for decay to become established. In most modern buildings in Europe the site is covered with a layer of concrete, but even good quality concrete allows a certain amount of moisture to pass through. In the U.S.A. many houses were built during and since the Second World War without a basement and having only a "crawl space" under them. The soil below the house was left exposed and moisture evaporating from the soil condensed in the flooring, especially in cold weather when the vents were often closed. It was found that this evaporation could be greatly reduced and the moisture content of the floor kept below the danger point by covering the surface of the ground with smooth surfaced roll roofing (weighing 55 lb per 108 ft^2), laid with an overlap of two inches at the joints. In any case ventilation must be provided so that the moisture can be carried away by a current of fresh air. A high proportion of the outbreaks of dry rot in suspended (hollow) floors is due to the absence of proper ventilation beneath them. Even when ventilating air bricks have been provided in the external walls they are frequently wrongly placed and too small in size. Often they are put in so near the ground level that the openings soon become blocked up with dead leaves, earth, cobwebs and so on. Sometimes they are even deliberately blocked by the occupants who have found the floors cold and draughty.

If ventilation under a floor is defective and a tendency to damp already exists, covering the upper surface of the boards with linoleum, cork carpet, rubber sheeting or parquet will soon render it really damp and seriously increase the risk of decay. These coverings can, however, be safely laid on properly constructed floors that are provided with adequate ventilation, and they are very unlikely ever to cause trouble on floors in the upper storeys. Condensation above ground-floor level seldom gives trouble in dwelling-houses though it does occasionally occur in rooms without a chimney, especially if the windows and doors have been carefully rendered draught-proof. It is very much more likely to be a source of trouble in industrial buildings, as will be explained presently.

In solid floors, constructed so that there is no air space between the wooden flooring and the site concrete, many cases of decay have occurred. It is essential to have an effective damp-proof course between the concrete and the flooring, as a certain amount of moisture will always rise through concrete in contact with the ground. (See Section on Prevention of Dry Rot, below.) Rot in solid boarded floors is usually caused by *Coniophora*, the Cellar Fungus.

DECAY OF WOODWORK IN INDUSTRIAL BUILDINGS

Many industrial operations, such as brewing, dyeing and jam-making, cause large quantities of steam to be discharged into the air, resulting in a very humid atmosphere in the factory. For some processes, such as spinning and weaving, the atmosphere may even have to be artificially humidified. Then, if there are cold surfaces, the moisture will condense on these, soon bringing the moisture content of any wood in contact with them above the danger level. Condensation is particularly likely to occur on the roofs, if these are not properly insulated. Severe and widespread rot caused by a fungus *Poria* sp. has been found in several weaving factories where the roof consisted of asbestos tiles lying directly over wooden boarding. During the winter, moisture condensed on the cold roof boards to such an extent that it ran down the walls. In one case the entire roof of a large weaving-shed was completely decayed within ten years of its erection. This trouble can largely be prevented by the provision of adequate insulation, in the right place, but to ensure complete freedom from any risk of decay structural wood used in a humidified building should be impregnated with a water-soluble preservative before being built in.

When setting out to provide insulation for a roof it must be remembered that it is no good fixing insulating boards to the underside of a sheet-metal roof if they are themselves going to become saturated with moisture. Insulating boards made from organic materials decay readily if they remain in a damp condition for any length of time, and in any case their insulating value decreases if they become wet. They should therefore be protected from condensation by the insertion of a moisture-proof layer between them and the air in the building. Existing old buildings are sometimes adapted for use as factories, and, if processes are carried on in them that involve the discharge of much moisture into the air, trouble with rot in the roof is likely to occur. Caution should therefore be exercised if air humidification is introduced into any existing building which has not been protected against the results of condensation.

An unusual case of condensation occurred in a swimming-bath where "acoustic tiling" had been fixed to a cold wall. Condensation on the wall behind the tiling was heavy in the cold weather, and set up rot in the battens to which the tiling was fixed. Another interesting outbreak of rot in a swimming-bath occurred during the war when the main bath was left full of water to act as a static water tank. The portable dance-floor which was normally laid over the empty bath during the winter was found, after a few years of lying over a full bath, to be extensively decayed as a result of moisture rising from the water below condensing in the floor boarding.

Another place where dry rot can be very troublesome is in the woodwork of cold stores, particularly in fruit stores where the temperature inside the store is not sufficiently low to check all fungal growth. Even if the inner lining, which is in contact with the air in the store, is too cold for fungus growth, the outer part of the framing and the insulation may remain above the temperature necessary to check fungal decay. All the structural woodwork used in the construction of a cold store, and its linings, should be thoroughly treated, preferably by impregnation, with a water-soluble preservative. In most of the larger cold stores used for meat and dairy produce little structural timber is now used; but the smaller stores erected on fruit farms for the cool storage of the fruit are still usually made of wood, and in some of these severe outbreaks of dry rot have occurred.

PREVENTION OF DECAY IN BUILDINGS

Since the fungi that cause decay in buildings can attack

timber only if it becomes and remains damp, the prevention of dry rot is almost entirely a matter of preventing moisture from reaching the woodwork. Dampness may result either from neglect to maintain a building in good repair or from faulty design and poor workmanship in its original construction. One may regard outbreaks of dry rot due to neglected maintenance as accidental and those due to bad design and shoddy buildings as chronic and inherent. The latter type is, of course, the most difficult to cure. Obviously if the original layout and construction of the building are such as to encourage dampness a higher standard of maintenance will be necessary than is required in a building that is well designed and made of first class materials. For example, window-sills that are made of Oak will not decay readily even if repainting is delayed longer than is really desirable; whereas if they are made of a perishable softwood they must be kept continually painted if rot is to be prevented.

Maintenance

If the following precautions are observed the risk of dry rot in any reasonably well-constructed building will be small.

Regularly examine the condition of all guttering and down pipes. Have any defects therein remedied without delay. See that overflow pipes do not drip on to walls.

Have leaves and dirt cleared at least once a year from all gullies, parapet and valley gutters.

See that the soil level is not allowed to rise above the damp-proof course in any part of the house.

See that openings in air bricks ventilating the sub-floor spaces are kept free from obstruction.

Do not lay impervious covering on any floors that show a tendency to dampness.

Do not store quantities of damp firewood in cellars and basements.

Many serious outbreaks of dry rot, followed in some cases by infestation with Death-Watch Beetle, have occurred in churches through failure to keep the roofs and guttering in a sound watertight condition. If money for maintenance is scarce, spend what is available on keeping out the wet, as failure to do this will invariably lead to far higher expenditure in the end. Again and again one sees that hundreds and thousands of pounds are needed for the repair of damage caused by dry rot, or Death-Watch Beetle, which could easily have been prevented by spending a few pounds at an earlier date on the maintenance of roofs and guttering.

Precautions in Construction

It is beyond the scope of this book to describe in full detail all the precautions that should be taken by architects and builders to ensure that no damp reaches the woodwork in any building which they may erect. But anyone who is concerned with the planning and erection of new buildings should appreciate the necessity for a careful scrutiny of plans and specifications that relate to the woodwork. Many outbreaks of dry rot originating in ground floors are the result of faulty construction.

Ground floors are of two types—suspended (or "hollow") and solid. Prior to the Second World War suspended floors, consisting of boarding nailed to joists resting on the footings of the main walls or on dwarf sleeper walls, were the most usual form of construction, and there is still a strong prejudice in their favour. Owing to the shortage of timber after the war solid ground floors were generally laid in dwelling houses, except on steeply sloping sites, and there is much to be said in their favour as they greatly reduce heat loss through the floor, and they cannot harbour vermin. They are in general use in many European countries, Austria and Switzerland for example.

Suspended Floors

The following are among the more important precautions to be taken when constructing suspended floors:

The earth below the floor should be covered with a bed of hardcore over which a layer of dense, well tamped concrete should be laid. In Scotland a layer of bituminous material is often used for this purpose. In the United States a covering of the site with good quality roofing felt has been found effectively to reduce evaporation from the soil and thus to keep the flooring dry.

To prevent the joists from touching brickwork into which soil moisture can rise there must be a damp-proof course in the dwarf walls as well as in the main walls, and there should be at least nine inches clear space between the bottom of the joists and the site concrete. It is important that no wooden shavings and debris should be left on the site.

Through ventilation must be provided under the suspended floor to carry off the moisture rising off the site concrete. If parts of a building are built with solid floors it is essential that pipes should be placed in the solid portions so that air can flow through them to the outside air. It is practically useless to make openings only along one wall of a room as air moves properly under a floor only if there are openings on *opposite* sides. This point is frequently overlooked when additional rooms with solid floors are added to houses in which the rest of the floors are suspended, as is likely to happen at the present time. (See Fig. 52.)

The air vents that are built into the external walls are usually too few and too small, the amount of actual open space in the average terra-cotta air brick often being less than 10 per cent of its total area. It is difficult to lay down any definite rate for the amount of under-floor ventilation that is desirable as this depends a great deal on local conditions. As a rough guide, $1 \frac{1}{2}$ in.^{2} of open area per foot run of external wall has been

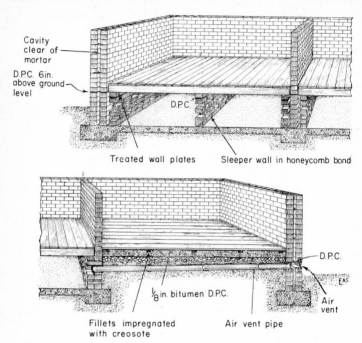

Cavity clear of mortar

D.P.C. 6in. above ground level

D.P.C.

Treated wall plates

Sleeper wall in honeycomb bond

D.P.C.

$\frac{1}{8}$ in. bitumen D.P.C.

Fillets impregnated with creosote

Air vent pipe

Air vent

Fig. 52. Section through house showing methods for insulating timbers against rising damp, and means for providing direct through ventilation under floors. The two diagrams are continuous. D.P.C. = Damp-proof course.

recommended for rooms of average size; but since the area below a floor which is giving off moisture increases as the square of the length of the boundary walls the total area of the floor must be taken into consideration, and a figure of 1 in^2 of clear opening per 4 ft^2 of floor area has been suggested as an absolute minimum. Air vents should not be close to the ground level as, if they are, they will quickly become blocked up.

Ground-floor joists should receive preservative treatment. In large buildings, such as gymnasia and drill-halls, in buildings under which adequate sub-floor ventilation cannot be provided owing to the nature of the site, and in buildings on badly drained, damp sites the treatment should involve impregnation under pressure. Under average conditions surface treatment should be adequate. The minimum should involve dipping, or thoroughly brushing, the ends of the joists where they are to come into contact with the brickwork. Wall plates should invariably be treated throughout their length. The underside of the floor boards themselves should receive a brush treatment.

Solid Floors

Solid floors finished in wood usually consist either of boards fixed to wooden battens embedded in the concrete or of wood blocks set in mastic. With the first type it is essential that the fixing battens should be *impregnated*, with a creosote or a water-soluble preservative, and that an effective damp-proof course be laid between the site concrete and the boarding. A membrane of bitumen poured hot (not a bituminous emulsion) at least $1/8$ in. thick at the thinnest point should be regarded as the minimum. Probably the most convenient place for this is immediately below the floor boards.

Wood blocks are usually fixed with sufficient bitumastic to protect them from rising damp, but some builders like to insert a damp-proof course sandwiched in the site concrete as an additional precaution.

Impervious coverings should never be laid on solid floors until the boarding has dried out.

External Joinery

So long as it is possible to maintain an unbroken film of paint over all joinery exposed to the weather it will remain free of infection and decay, but with the seasonal changes in moisture content joints are liable to open up and admit moisture

211

and fungus spores. Formerly the best joinery timbers were selected so that little or no porous sapwood was included. To-day, however, most of the softwood used for joinery is cut out from small sized logs and therefore some sapwood is almost invariably present. This has a low resistance to decay, and it absorbs moisture very readily so that the overlying film of paint becomes loosened and disintegrates. The author has seen quite extensive repairs rendered necessary through decay of external door and window frames in supposedly well built houses less than ten years old. Among the most vulnerable points are the bottom faces of door posts standing on concrete, as these cannot ever be repainted after erection. It is a wise precaution to steep window frames, and external doors and door frames, in a water-repellent solvent-type preservative, *before* they are erected and painted.

External doors exposed to the weather, especially large doors for garages, should be built so as to shed rain water, preferably with all the external joints between the boards running vertically so that the water can drain away freely. Rails, braces and mouldings are best placed on the inside face of the door, as if they are on the outside they trap moisture between themselves and the vertical members. The concrete threshold below such doors should be sloped down so that water drains way from under the door.

Wide eaves with a good overhang provide a great deal of protection to wooden siding and to casement type windows on upper stories. It is very noticeable how well preserved are many of the ancient wooden buildings in the Alps where wide eaves have been provided.

Roofs

In the normal pitched roof there is sufficient circulation of air to keep the timber dry, and even if occasional slight leakage occurs there is little risk of dry rot as the wood can

212

rapidly dry out again. Trouble is much more likely to occur in a flat timber roof, particularly if it is bounded by a parapet wall, and all the timbers in such roofs should be impregnated with preservative. As parapet walls are a frequent cause of dampness and decay it is most important that a damp-proof course should be inserted, both below the coping in case leakage through the joints of the coping should occur, and at the foot of the parapet wall just above the roof level.

Choice of Timber

In the great majority of houses built before World War II the timber used for carcassing and joinery was a softwood, the most usual being Baltic Redwood (Red Deal), Whitewood (Spruce), and Douglas Fir (Columbian Pine). Only in churches and monumental buildings, and in really old houses, did one find roofing timbers and joists made of hardwood (usually Oak); though in better class property hardwood was often used for block and strip flooring. After the war, however, light hardwoods, mainly West African timbers such as Abura, were used to a limited extent for structural purposes. There is, of course, great variation between the different species, and though some of them are well suited for the purpose they cannot indiscriminately be substituted for softwoods. Obeche, for instance, is a good timber for shop fittings but is unsuitable for joists. Though some are durable others are more readily attacked by dry rot than is good quality Baltic Redwood, and these should receive preservative treatment if they are to be used in any situation where there is the slightest risk of damp. In many of these hardwoods there is a wide band of sapwood, hence they are liable to infestation by Powder-post Beetles (*Lyctus* spp.) and for this reason alone they should receive preservative treatment.

Whether the species chosen be a hardwood or a softwood only timber free from any trace of incipient decay should be

213

used for building, though there is no objection to material showing a certain amount of blue stain in the sapwood. Many of the older specifications used to call for timber not only free from blue stain but from sapwood also. Today such exclusiveness would be impracticable as much of the softwood now used comes from small diameter second-growth trees which must, of necessity, contain a fairly high proportion of sapwood. Though it is just as strong as heartwood and there is no objection to its presence it must be remembered that it is much less durable. It absorbs preservatives readily and there is much to be said for giving preservative treatment to any structural timbers containing a high proportion of sapwood, especially those intended for floor joists. Apart from the risk of fungal decay, there is always the possibility that the timber will at some later date be exposed to infestation by furniture beetles to which sapwood is also very susceptible. On account of its susceptibility to insect attack sapwood of Oak should be rigidly excluded from monumental buildings.

To use the words of so many optimistic specifications, "the timber shall be well seasoned" before it is used for building purposes. But this well-worn, vague phrase is capable of various interpretations, and if really dry timber is wanted a definite maximum moisture content should be inserted in the specification. Ideally, only thoroughly air-dried timber having a moisture content of not more than 20 per cent should be used for general building purposes, while the moisture content of high-class joinery, wood block and strip flooring should be down to about 12 per cent. In practice, however, it may be virtually impossible to adhere rigidly to this rule. How much deviation can safely be allowed depends a good deal on what opportunity the timber will have to dry out subsequently in position in the building. Rafters that will be frequently exposed in a roof have a far better chance to dry out than have wall plates or joists in a ground floor. It is easier for the boards

214

in a suspended floor to dry out in position than it is for flooring fixed down closely in a solid floor.

Every effort should be made to ensure that timber that is to be used in the construction of the ground floor should be as well seasoned and as dry as possible, and if the moisture content of the wood is found appreciably to exceed 20-22 per cent when it is delivered on the site, it should be stacked openly under cover to dry out before it is used.

It is useless to have dry seasoned timber delivered on to a site and then to leave it exposed to rain for several weeks, during which time it may absorb enough water to raise its moisture content far above the danger point for dry rot. Timber piled in the open on a building site should always be protected by tarpaulins in wet weather.

Paint should never be applied to joinery made of imperfectly seasoned wood until it has dried out. If, in an emergency, some form of decorative finish has to be applied to new woodwork before it has dried out a flat paint that will permit moisture to pass through it should be used and never a high-gloss paint that will retain the moisture.

LEGAL ASPECTS

Disputes sometimes arise between owners of property and their tenants as to responsibility for making good damage caused by dry rot during an occupancy. Many buildings were requisitioned during the war by Government departments and upon relinquishment were found to be affected by dry rot, and claims were made to meet the cost of repairs. Some of these claims were for very considerable sums; for instance, in one case that came up before the Scottish Courts, a sum of £ 45,000 was claimed to repair damage in a requisitioned Scottish castle. In such disputes the owner may try to establish that the occupier, either by his actions or by neglect, has rendered the building liable to dry rot, while the occupier may attempt to show that the rot was already present in the building, or that it developed as a result of faulty construction. Sometimes a compromise is reached in which the cost of repairs is shared according to the degree of "aggravation" of dry rot known to have been already present when the building was taken over, but it is often extremely difficult to arrive at a fair decision as to the degree of responsiblity that should fall on either party.

There is frequently considerable argument as to whether the rot started before or after the tenant became responsible, and in this connection the question—so often asked is—how can one tell how long dry rot has been present in a building, or in any particular piece of wood? The answer is that a really precise estimate can seldom be given, as the rate of development of the Dry Rot Fungus depends so much on the kind of wood on which it is growing, the moisture content of the wood, and the temperature at which it has been kept. If fruiting bodies of *Merulius* are found, and if the strands have penetrated deeply into the brickwork, it is unlikely that the outbreak is less than two to three years old, while complete decay of large sized timbers, beams and joists will not take place under about three years' exposure to attack. If the wood has darkened and the fungal growths look old, dusty and damaged by insects the attack may have existed for five, ten, or even more years. Sometimes all traces of mycelium on the surface of the decayed wood disappear in the course of time, so that when no such signs of fungus growth are visible it can usually be assumed that the attack started many years ago.

But beyond saying that an outbreak is of recent origin or is of long standing it becomes a matter of either informed judgement or frank guesswork to estimate the approximate age of any case of extensive dry rot. Bearing in mind, however, that this rot can only develop if there has been persistent dampness, the important evidence to be obtained is that which relates to the time, place and extent of the entry of moisture, and any actions or neglect likely to have influenced the moisture content of the woodwork. Such evidence, coupled with the extent of the fungal growth and the amount of rot present, and considered in conjunction with any available reports of the condition of the building before the tenant's occupancy, will help an expert in such matters to place responsibility on the right shoulders.

Disputes also sometimes arise after the sale of a building if a purchaser claims that the condition of the property has been misrepresented. In 1934, Mr. Justice du Parcq awarded damages of £150 to a purchaser who found decay in a house which he had been assured by the vendor was completely free from dry rot. Occasionally in such cases, if the house has been professionally surveyed, the purchaser may bring an action against the surveyor. A judgment given by Lord Birnam in 1949 in the Glasgow Court of Session is of interest in this connection:

"His Lordship held that negligence on the part of the surveyor had not been proved, and said that he accepted that the possibility of dry rot was a thing that always ought to be present in the mind of a surveyor, and that he should be on the lookout for any evidence that might, to his skilled mind, be suggestive of dry rot; but he was unable to accept the view that, in such circumstances, his duty required him, in the absence of any suspicious circumstances, to cause carpets and linoleum to be lifted, and to go underneath floors and make a detailed examination of every hidden corner of the building."

The words "in the absence of suspicious circumstances" seem significant; it might have been considered culpable negligence to omit a careful search for dry rot if the walls were obviously saturated from overflowing rain pipes!

Claims have sometimes been made against firms of builders or decorators when dry rot has appeared in a building in consequence of work which they have carried out. In such a case brought before the High Court in Birmingham in 1951, Mr. Justice Humphreys held that a furnishing firm who had recommended the use of linoleum on a solid boarded floor, which subsequently decayed, were responsible for the cost of its reconstruction. It was agreed that the floor in question had no damp-proof layer between the boarding and the concrete, but the defendants were blamed for having made no inspection and asked no questions about the construction before making their recommendations. The judgment was upheld when the case was taken to the Court of Appeal.

It is to be hoped, with a better understanding of the causes of dry rot and of the conditions which lead to its development, occasions for such disputes will arise less frequently in the future.

CHAPTER 11

Protection of Timber in Farm and Garden

IN AGRICULTURE and horticulture, timber, in various forms, is used in quite large quantities, and it seems a pity that so much of it is allowed prematurely to decay. Even if a considerable proportion of the timber used on farms and estates is home grown and its cost does not therefore appear as an outgoing from the estate, the time spent on its fellings, preparation and erection becomes a direct charge on the labour bill. Labour that can ill be spared from other urgent work has to be devoted to the repair of fencing, gates and buildings.

On many farms and estates little or no naturally durable timber, such as Oak, Larch and Sweet Chestnut, is grown or, if it once was, the supply has now become exhausted, and recourse is had to much less durable kinds which decay in a few years. By preservative treatment it is possible to render woods such as Beech, Sycamore, Elm, Willow, Lime and Alder quite as durable as the most resistant species, thereby allowing the more durable and valuable timbers to be put to more profitable use.

There is considerable variation in the resistance to decay of even the more durable species, depending on the amount of sapwood present and on the rate of growth of the tree, whereas any timber that has been thoroughly treated can be relied on to give good service. It is worth-while treating even relatively durable timbers such as Larch, for even though the heartwood may not absorb much preservative any sapwood present will be protected, and the risk of premature decay of the heartwood will be minimized.   Pressure-creosoted sapwood of almost all species will last longer than will the heartwood of the most durable home-grown timber.

Fencing

Surface application of preservative is of little value on timber that is to be permanently in contact with the earth.   Poles and posts should therefore be given an impregnation treatment. Where maximum life is required it is best to use timber that has been creosoted under pressure in a cylinder, but for most estate and farm purposes impregnation of the posts and rails with creosote by the open tank process gives adequate and sufficiently lasting protection, provided that the wood is [reasonably permeable.   Butt treatment is often quite adequat efor fence posts and, when treated in this way, they can be expected to last several times longer than untreated ones, especially if the part above ground level is given an occasional brush over with creosote in hot dry weather.

Creosote is generally the most economical and effective preservative to use on fencing, but for special purposes, where a clean finish, over which paint can subsequently be applied, is desirable, a preservative of the copper-chrome arsenic type can successfully be used.

As far as possible no cuts should be made into the treated posts, and they should be handled with care to avoid any severe abrasion.   If it is essential to cut into the posts, or if any accidental damage should occur, then the untreated wood thus exposed should be thoroughly brushed with hot creosote.   After treatment the posts should be piled openly so that the preservative dries off the surface, and they will then be in a cleaner condition to handle when they are erected.   Posts that have received only butt treatment should not be left for long lying in contact with the ground.

At one time it was a common practice to char the ends of

220

posts in a fire before setting them in the ground. This treatment was supposed to make them last much longer, as the
layer of charcoal was thought to provide a barrier against the
entry of wood-rotting fungi. While it is true that charcoal
itself is resistant to decay, and even perhaps mildly antiseptic,
such treatment does not actually help much to extend the life
of the posts. During the setting of them in the ground the
superficial layer of charcoal is usually damaged and unburnt
wood exposed to infection; and though when the charred ends
of the posts are subsequently dipped into creosote somewhat
better results can be obtained, the treatment does not give
anything like as good protection as does impregnation of the butts.

At the present time it is very difficult to estimate, even
approximately, the cost of treating posts, owing to frequent
changes in the price of labour and materials; but it can safely
be said that, *in relation to the value of the timber itself*, the extra
cost of treatment is less than it was before the war. In other
words, the value of timber has increased more than the cost
of the preservative and the treatment. It therefore follows
that it is even more worth-while treating timber with preservative
now than it was in pre-war days when timber was relatively
cheap. Mr. Milne Home put the case for wood preservation
very cogently in the following words:

"I think an important point is this—that if you use untreated wood for fencing stakes you will have to put in at least three,
and possibily four, to equal the life of one creosoted stake.
If you take it as low as three, and calculate the labour involved
in doing three times over what you would otherwise only require to do once, you will see that the small additional expense
of using creosote as a preservative is very well-spent money."

Where the number of posts to be treated does not warrant
the erection of a treating drum for hot and cold treatment, the

posts should be barked and stacked so that they season, and they should then be stood upright in a can of creosote, or other preservative, for several weeks, during which time a considerable quantity of liquid will be absorbed; they should be immersed in the fluid to a depth slightly greater than that to which they will be stood in the ground.

Another and perhaps the simplest and cheapest way of protecting posts from decay is to drill an inch-wide hole into the butt end to a depth of 9 in., and to pack this firmly with copper sulphate crystals, and then plug if firmly with a dowel or cork. The salts will slowly dissolve in the moisture entering from the soil and be carried up the centre of the pole. The surface of the post should be thoroughly brushed over with creosote to protect it until diffusion of the salts begins to take place. Posts treated in this way may show some decay on the surface but a sound core should remain for a very long time.

Gates

Though gates are normally made of Oak heartwood it is all too common to see them broken down, due to failure at the joints where moisture has penetrated and permitted decay to become established. If a sufficiently large tank is available the gates can be impregnated after assembly, otherwise each piece, after it is fashioned to its final size, should be impregnated with, or steeped in, creosote. Gates that are to be painted should be impregnated with a water-borne preservative, or thoroughly brushed with a solvent type, paying particular attention to the end grain as that is where moisture and decay first gain entry.

Other Uses for Treated Timber on Farms

Fencing and gates are by no means the only woodwork on a farm that is well worth-while to treat. Barn roofs and floors, which are often constructed of waney-edged timbers containing a high proportion of sapwood, are all too frequently severely damaged by wood-boring beetles and decay, and have to be repaired at considerable cost. Treatment of such timbers before the building is erected (and at intervals subsequently, if the treatment has only been a superficial one) will always be a good investment and insurance against expense and trouble in the future.

The woodwork in pigsties, byres and stables should also be treated and no ill effects on stock have been reported, even when animals were brought into freshly creosoted buildings. Mangers and feeding-troughs can also safely be creosoted, but obviously the creosote must be allowed to dry off before food is put into them. It would however be unwise to use any strong-smelling preservative anywhere in a dairy as milk, butter and cheese easily become tainted.

Wooden chicken-houses should always receive thorough treatment with a preservative both inside and out, but poultry should not be introduced into a freshly creosoted house. A few weeks after treatment, when the fumes have evaporated, the birds can be brought in without the slightest risk.

Horticultural Uses for Treated Timber

There are many uses for treated timber in horticulture in addition to those suggested for the farms. In most gardens there are wooden potting-sheds and sheds for the storage of tools which should receive regular treatment with a tar-oil preservative or a creosote-tar mixture. Untreated stakes for young fruit trees and ornamental shrubs can never be used a second time, and seldom even last until the plants no longer need their support. Pergola posts, even those cut from larch, last only a few years, as they are usually cut from thinnings that contain little heartwood. When new stakes cost very little to buy and labour was cheap, treatment was seldom considered worth-while, but under present-day conditions, when

223

both timber and labour are so expensive, there can be no question that it pays well to treat all such stakes and posts.

Some caution should be exercised in bringing freshly creosoted stakes into proximity with young trees and shrubs. During a discussion held in 1938 by the British Wood Preserving Association on the preservative treatment of garden timber, differing views were expressed as to the degree of risk involved in using freshly creosoted wood in a garden. Some speakers reported that they had never seen any damage caused thereby, while others quoted instances of the roots of fruit trees having been killed on the side adjacent to creosoted posts and of rose trees dying from the same cause. It is likely that both the composition of the creosote and the nature of the soil affect the issue, and it is probable that there is much less risk of trouble in a chalky soil which will help to neutralize the tar acids from the creosote. The general opinion seems to be that the risk of damage to trees and shrubs from creosoted stakes is very slight provided that the treated wood is allowed to weather for a few weeks before being used, and that the trunk of the tree is protected from direct contact with the post by means of sacking or some other packing material. When it is necessary to use stakes within a few days of treatment it is safer to use a preservative based on copper naphthenate. Stakes for tomatoes should never be creosoted as this plant seems particularly sensitive to tar oils.

Greenhouses and Garden Frames

The woodwork in the traditional type of greenhouse is exposed to conditions which are very favourable for the growth of wood-rotting fungi, as the temperature and humidity are generally high. Once decay becomes established it may spread rapidly, particularly in houses where so-called "stove" plants are grown, and in houses for orchids and tropical ferns in which the humidity as well as the temperature are kept permanently high. True dry rot, caused by *Merulius lacrymans*, has not been found in a greenhouse, though it is not uncommon in conservatories adjoining houses. The most frequent cause of decay in greenhouse timbers is the fungus *Poria xantha* which flourishes at higher temperatures. It causes a brown crumbling rot and produces small poroid fruit bodies of pale sulphur colour and rather chalky consistency.

Orchid and tropical plant houses were formerly often built of Teak, which is an ideal timber for glass-house construction, combining great strength and durability, and "moving" very little with changes in moisture content; but at the same time it is very expensive. Similar timbers such as *Afrormosia* and Iroko would no doubt be very suitable, but they too are expensive and in rather short supply. Among tropical hardwoods Agba, Idigbo, and Red Meranti are good alternatives. Western Red Cedar, which is a light, straight-grained softwood, has a high resistance to decay, and has been used extensively for the construction of frames and greenhouses. It is not so strong as Baltic Redwood, and the dimensions in which it is used may therefore have to be adjusted accordingly. Greenhouses built of this wood will not last indefinitely if left quite untreated, and it is now the usual practice for builders to give this timber a brush treatment with a water repellent preservative that will help to retain the natural preservatives in the wood. Oak has also been used to a limited extent, but, though durable, it is rather liable to distort unless perfectly straight-grained material is chosen, and, of course, any distortion of glazing bars is most undesirable. It is, however, very suitable for the wall plates and staging. Durable timbers, such as Teak and Western Red Cedar, are sometimes left unpainted and given an occasional coat of linseed oil. But it is really better to paint even these woods, as more light is reflected from a painted surface. High quality selected Baltic Redwood or Douglas Fir free from sapwood will last extremely well *if the house is regularly painted* with good quality white-lead paint; but today not only is timber of that quality hard to come by, but maintenance is apt to be neglected owing to shortage of labour. The need for preservative treatment is therefore much more urgent than it was formerly, and, in fact, many firms are treating all the woodwork before it is painted.

Careful consideration should be given to the choice of preservative for greenhouse timber. It is much safer to avoid the tar-oil preservatives (creosotes) entirely, as some plants, such as tomatoes, are extremely sensitive to their fumes, and these may continue to evaporate from the treated wood for a considerable time whenever the woodwork gets really hot in the sunshine. Impregnation of the individual framing members and glazing bars, etc., with water-soluble preservative containing chromates, gives excellent protection, and woodwork thus treated can be painted after it has redried. If, however, the timber is not quite straight grained a certain amount of distortion may occur, and for this reason some manufacturers prefer to rely on surface applications of a solvent type preservative containing copper naphthenate. In woods that absorb preservatives fairly readily such treatment gives quite good protection, provided that the solution is applied generously and special attention is given to the cut ends. It is not, however, adequate for such perishable timbers as Obeche which should never be used for greenhouses unless they can be impregnated.

Whether the timbers have been treated with water soluble or solvent type preservative the greenhouses should afterwards be painted in the ordinary way; but under the very humid conditions usually maintained in them growth of mildew on the paint is sometimes troublesome. One particular mould, known as *Phoma pigmentivora*, causes a vivid purplish discoloration in white paint. Once this mould has got established it will spread rapidly causing spots, or wide areas, of purplish colour wherever condensation occurs. As it is from the oils in the paint that the mould derives its nourishment it is obviously useless just to apply a new coat. The only thing to do is to strip off the mouldy paint and sterilize the underlying wood with an aqueous fungicide such as a 5 per cent solution of sodium pentachlorophenate, and then to use a fungicidal paint for redecoration. Several paint firms market special fungicidal paints for this purpose.

Seed and Bulb Boxes

At one time seed boxes could be bought so cheaply that little interest was taken in their preservation, but at present-day prices there is no doubt that preservative treatment is economically more than justified. Even the relatively stout bulb boxes, made of good quality Baltic Redwood $3/_8$ in. thick, will decay in three seasons, while boxes made of thinner material often do not last, under commercial conditions, more than one, or at the most, two seasons. While in use these boxes are exposed to conditions extremely favourable for rapid decay as they are filled with a rich soil which is kept continually moist and warm, and when not in use they are often stacked in the open with a certain amount of soil left in them.

In a series of experiments by Moore and Bryan, reported in the *Journal of the Royal Horticultural Society* for March 1946, it was shown that none of the preservative treatments which they used, with the possible exception of sodium fluoride, had any noticeable ill effect on the growth or flowering of the bulbs. Creosote may cause damage to certain sensitive plants, and it is wiser never to use it for this purpose, but other equally effective preservatives are available. Water solubles, such as a 4 per cent solution of zinc chloride (6 oz to the gallon), or a 2 per cent copper sulphate (3 oz to the gallon) are very suitable, but if they are applied only by brushing or spraying the treatment should be repeated each year when the boxes are emptied. If the preservative is applied by a short hot and cold open-tank treatment

227

one initial treatment will protect the boxes for many years. In the tests referred to above all the boxes thus treated were serviceable after eight years. Solvent type preservatives are also well suited for this purpose, and in the tests all the boxes treated by dipping for 15 sec in a proprietary 25 per cent solution of copper naphthenate were still sound after ten years and thought then to be good probably for another five. Moore and Bryan found that boxes made with ordinary wire nails deteriorated earlier than did those pinned with galvanized nails, though in the boxes treated with copper naphthenate no difference was observed.

Few of the naturally resistant timbers are suitable for box-making as most of the durable hardwoods split so easily when nailed. However, Western Red Cedar (*Thuya plicata*), one of the few really durable softwoods, is ideal for seed boxes and has been increasingly used for this purpose. Boxes made from this timber may last without any treatment for ten years or more, but it is important that only galvanized nails be used in Western Red Cedar as it is particularly corrosive to wire nails. Whether the timber from home-grown trees of this species will prove as durable as the imported Canadian remains to be seen, but in any case its resistance will certainly be better than that of ordinary Pine and Spruce.

Mushroom Houses

Probably conditions in mushroom houses are more favourable for decay than those in any other type of horticultural building, for the fungi (mushrooms) that are cultivated in them are closely related to those which cause decay, and the same set of conditions favours the growth of both. The bed boards especially are liable to rapid decay and they also become infected with fungi, such as species of *Fusarium*, which are harmful to the mushrooms. It is therefore highly desirable that the boards should be treated with a preservative, and 2 per

Fig. 53. Dutch lights over mushroom beds attacked by a wood-rotting fungus, *Poria* sp.

cent copper sulphate has been found satisfactory for this purpose. Creosote, and creosote diluted with petrol, have also been tried, but damage to the succeeding crop of mushrooms was reported when the creosote was applied a short time before the compost was placed in the beds, and also when the oils contained a high proportion of volatile compounds. As a result of some laboratory tests carried out at Wye College, Pizer and Glassock concluded that solutions of copper sulphate, or of any of the following proprietary wood preservatives—Green Cuprinol, Celcure, or Wolman Triolith—could be used with negligible risk of damage to the mushroom crop. Western Red Cedar again is very suitable for construction of mushroom houses and no damage to the crop has been reported as a result of its use.

229

R

Minor Uses for Treated Wood in Gardens

When one begins to look around a garden or an estate with a critical eye it is surprising how many instances one can find of premature decay in wooden articles, much, if not all, of which could be prevented by the judicious use of preservatives. Wooden edging along garden paths and flower borders decays rapidly unless it is treated, and where considerable lengths of such edging are laid, as in public parks and pleasure gardens, their treatment would be a worth-while economy. Open tank treatment with creosote is the best for this purpose. Wooden labels can conveniently be treated by steeping them in a copper naphthenate solution, or other solvent type preservative, over which paint can subsequently be applied if desired.

Wheelbarrows, which are often left out in all weathers, and which are exposed to infection whenever they are used for carrying soil or manure, should be plentifully brushed with creosote during hot weather. All soil should first be carefully brushed out and the oil should be applied liberally so that it finds its way down into the joints.

Wooden handles of garden tools and implements should be painted with linseed oil before they are taken into use and given an occasional rub over with a rag soaked in this oil. It is safer not to use creosote on tool handles as some skins are sensitive to tar oils, especially when damp with sweat.

Beehives are liable to rot unless they are regularly painted, and here again Western Red Cedar is the ideal timber for their construction. When this wood is not available the exterior of the beehives should be given two brush-coats of a water soluble, or a solvent type preservative, and then left to dry off before being painted in the usual way.

CHAPTER 12

Decay in Ships, Boats and Marine Works

In the days when all warships, as well as merchantmen, were constructed throughout of wood, dry rot of their timbers sometimes threatened the very security of England. It is not therefore surprising that the first serious attempts to understand the causes of decay and to discover means for its prevention were undertaken by those responsible for His Majesty's ships of war. Dr. Ramsbottom has written a most interesting account* of these early endeavours from which many of the following historical references have been taken.

The design of the wooden warships changed very slowly and was always limited to some extent by the size of the trees and from quite an early date certain parts of the ship's frame required the largest oaks available. There was then little question of ships becoming obsolete and their length of life depended mainly on the durability of the timbers. H.M.S. *Victory* was already 40 years old at the Battle of Trafalgar.

Historical

When Queen Elizabeth I came to the throne she found that 10 out of the 32 Royal ships were decayed. Under James I a commission of inquiry, reporting on the condition of the Navy, drew attention to the importance of seasoning the timber before it was used. It was said that ships made from unseasoned timber had to be repaired within 6 or 7 years after construction

---

* *Essex Naturalist*, **25**, 231-267 (1937).

instead of lasting 20 or more as they should have done. Under Charles II a considerable programme of new building was undertaken, but there was great difficulty in finding the necessary timber and Pepys remarked, "But God knows where the materials can be had for so many first and second rates however we shall think fit to propose the building of them". Rearmament had its problems then as in a later century! After these new ships had been built it was found that many had begun to decay even before they were taken into service, and it was reported that

> " the greatest part nevertheless of these 30 ships (without ever having looked out of harbour) were let to sink into such distress through decay contracted in their buttocks, quarters, bows, thickstuff without board and spirkettings upon their gun decks... that several of them lye in danger of sinking at their very moorings. "

Pepys fully understood the importance of ventilation and of keeping the rainwater out of a ship. In one of his reports he writes:

> "Their holds not cleared or aired but (for want of gratings and opening their hatches and scuttles) suffered to heat and moulder, till I have with my own hands gathered toadstools growing, in the most considerable of them, as big as my fists... Port ropes also wanting wherewith to open the ports for airing them in dry weather and scuppers upon their gun decks, in wet, to prevent the sinking of rain through their shrunken seams into their holds and among their timbers. "

During the whole of the 18th century trouble with dry rot continued. When Lord Sandwich visited the ships in reserve in 1771 masses of fungus had to be dug out before the timbers could be inspected.   During the American War of Independence 66 ships of the Royal Navy foundered, probably from this cause.   At the court martial following the sinking at Portsmouth of the *Royal George* it was disclosed that her bottom fell out when she was being heeled over for a slight repair, some of the oak panels being so rotten that they could not hold the sheathing nails and split apart.

Much importance was attached to the felling of Oak in the winter, and the excellent condition of the timbers in the *Royal Sovereign* fifty years after she was built was attributed to the fact that the trees used in her construction had been winter felled, but this view was not substantiated in other vessels.

It was after Trafalgar, when large numbers of ships had been built of absolutely green timber, that dry rot in the Navy assumed really alarming proportions, and at the Peace it was stated that half the ships were in a rotten condition.   Some great men-of-war containing over 3000 loads of timber became useless in two or three years.   The naval authorities became seriously disturbed and the celebrated botanist, James Sowerby, was asked to examine and report on the condition of the notorious *Queen Charlotte*, a first rate of 110 guns, which rotted so quickly that she had to be largely rebuilt before she could even be commissioned.   Within 14 months of her launching in 1810 all the planking, both within and without board, together with many of the timber and beams, had to be removed.   Repairs up to 1816 cost £94,499 in addition to the original cost of £88,534 before she could be used, and by 1859, when her name was changed to the *Excellent* (a whimsical choice, as Ramsbottom observes), the total cost of repairs had amounted to £287,837.

Ramsbottom (*loc. sit.*) quotes Sowerby's report in full, and fascinating reading it is to the modern student of timber decay, for the latter's observations are acute and his recommendations are sound.   He listed and illustrated a considerable number of fungi that he found, noting that *Boletus* (*Merulius*) *lacrymans*

233

was rare. All through his report he insists on the importance of allowing free access of air to all parts of the ship, and suggests that the humidity of the air in various parts of the ships should be tested by means of hygrometers, and that when it was found to exceed a certain figure steps should be taken to increase the ventilation. He also stressed the need to season the timber before it was used and described precisely how it should be stacked so that it would season to the best advantage.

When it was realized how extensive the rot was in the Navy many people came forward with suggestions for its prevention and cure, and various preservative treatments, none of them very effective, were proposed and tried. Probably one of the reasons for the failure of some of the more toxic chemicals that were tested was the high resistance of Oak heartwood to the penetration of any preservative fluid. Packing the timbers with common salt was often tried and this practice was continued for a long time and probably did afford some protection to the timber, as wood that contains a sufficiently high concentration of salt has a fair resistance to fungal decay. When the old *Implacable* was examined by the author some years ago before it was decided that she was beyond repair, he found that though the whole of the hull above the water was severely decayed, the timbers in the bilge, which were more or less pickled with salt from the sea water, were still largely sound.

It was often suggested that ships should be sunk and then refloated after a period of several months' immersion in sea water, and this treatment was in fact found to arrest fungal decay, but it did not afford any permanent protection because the amount of salt absorbed by the timbers was insufficient. Ambrose Bowden of the Navy Office, who published a treatise on dry rot in 1815, claimed the merit of having discovered this method. While the practical advice he gave was in general good it scarcely justified his rather smug statement in 1818: "It is with infinite satisfaction that I reflect on having discovered

234

a simple, easy, cheap and effective remedy for a decay which has consumed the Navy for many years past."

Despite Mr. Ambrose Bowden, dry rot continued to be a problem in the Navy until the coming of the ironclads. It was, of course, by no means confined to the men-of-war. It was said that East India merchantmen seldom made more than four, and sometimes only three, round trips to India before they became almost useless from decay.

DECAY IN MODERN CRAFT

Although, with a few rare exceptions, no large ships have been constructed from timber for a long time past, there are, of course, still great numbers of smaller craft built of wood, varying from large fishing vessels and ocean-going yachts down to dinghies and punts. There is no doubt that the cost of repairing damage caused in these by fungal decay amounts to a very considerable sum, possibly of the order of £2,000,000 a year.

The upkeep of boats, like that of houses, was neglected during the war and many craft were laid up for long periods, very often under rather poor conditions of storage. It was therefore not surprising that decay became more prevalent during and immediately after the war years. In parts of the U.S.A. fishermen estimate that as much decay can take place during one year when a boat is laid up idle as during five years in service.

M. G. Duff has surveyed* the extent of the problem of rot in yachts and boats, and reference should be made to his original papers by anyone interested in the improvements in constructional details from the point of view of decay prevention. He found that there is little serious decay in undecked open

---

* *Ship and Boat Builder* **5**, and **6** (1951-2).

boats, but in decked boats, most of which were yachts, he found decay in 67 out of 86 craft he examined, and in 46 of these he found it could be described as severe.

Distribution of Rot in Boats

Duff studied the distribution of the decay in different parts of the vessels and found that the main areas liable to decay are at deck level, and internally in the bilge area below the cabin sole or flooring. Decay in the deck structures above main deck level, which are fully exposed to the air, and in the hull itself, was less common and less severe. He concluded that deck leakage was a primary cause of trouble and found that the structural members most usually attacked were the beam shelves, beam knees, beam ends, carlines, half-beams and frame heads.

In the bilges decay occurs mainly as a result of condensation of moisture that has evaporated from the bilge water. In sea-going vessels the bilge water is salt, and this salinity is sufficient to retard attack by ordinary wood-rotting fungi. Therefore decay of timber in the bilge areas is likely to be more serious in vessels operating in fresh water. The provision of good ventilation to the bilge spaces will assist greatly in keeping the surface of the timbers dry and will reduce the risk of fungal infection becoming established.

Decay of masts and spars is rare as the wood is fully exposed and can dry off quickly. When it does occur it will generally be confined to the part where the mast passes through the deck, and to the place where the hounds are fixed. To prevent moisture from entering at deck level a watertight jacket should be fitted around the mast. In addition, the wedges should be steeped in preservative and the mast itself and adjacent beam and deck structure thoroughly brushed with preservative. Similarly, if wooden hounds are used they should be soaked in a wood preservative.

236

Use of Unsound Timber

When deep-seated decay is found in members of large size such as stern posts, the presence of incipient decay in the timber before it was used must be suspected. Several instances of severe brown cubical rot in the Oak stern posts in ships' lifeboats were found to have been caused by *Polyporus sulphureus*, a fungus that attacks standing Oaks. Evidently the posts had been cut from trees that contained heart rot, and this had not been entirely eliminated during the conversion of the logs. Hyphæ of a wood-rotting fungus may be present in apparently sound wood beyond the area that is softened and discoloured, and so it is essential when converting logs that contain heart rot to cut well beyond (18-24 in.) the last signs of attack. It should be noted that infection is likely to spread beyond the obviously decayed portions for a greater distance along than across the grain of the wood.

Timber used in a boat has less opportunity of drying out *in situ*, and of remaining dry, than timber used in a heated building. There is, therefore, a much greater risk of any traces of incipient decay continuing to spread and causing serious damage in boat timbers than in house timbers. For this reason it is essential that only timber which is completely sound, and free from any traces of incipient decay, should be employed in boat building.

When decay appears sporadically in various places in the timbers and stringers, and its occurrence seems to bear no relationship to penetration of moisture or to lack of ventilation, it may be suspected that infection was already present in those particular timbers when they were put in. As an example of this may be quoted the case of a fire launch that had been excellently maintained, and yet was found to have widespread rot in her rock-elm timbers within three years of having been launched. The only possible explanation for such rapid decay in a well-designed and maintained boat was that the timbers

237

were initially unsound. A good deal of rock elm was held in log form for long periods during the last war and became infected with dote before ever it was converted.

Douglas Fir (Columbian Pine) not infrequently contains traces of brown pocket rot caused by a fungus now known as *Poria monticola* (formerly considered a variety of *Trametes serialis*) which will continue to spread so long as the moisture content of the wood remains over 20 per cent. This fungus, which is not thought to be a species native to this country, has been identified on several occasions from decayed timber in boats. In America it has been found to be about the commonest and most destructive fungus of softwoods used in boats. The presence of incipient decay caused by this fungus may be difficult to detect as the pockets of dote are often internal, and no indication may be visible on the rough-sawn faces. Careful examination of the freshly cut end grain will however generally show up the pockets of dote as the grain in these pockets will break off short and pull out when the wood is cross-cut with a sharp saw.

Fungi Infecting Boats after Construction

Probably the commonest fungus found in boats is *Coniophora cerebella*, which has been found on both hard and softwoods and also on plywood. Various species of *Poria* also occur (See Fig. 54.) but *Merulius lacrymans* is seldom, if ever, found. It is likely that many other species would be recorded if cultures were prepared from samples of the decayed wood taken from boats, but as fungi rarely fructify in boats their identity remains undetected.

Constructional Features

The use of a double-skin hull is considered by many people as a frequent cause of rot. This type of construction has advantages from the point of view of strength, but it makes

Fig. 54. Growth of *Poria* sp. on underside
of floor boards over tanks in a motor boat.
C.C.R.

repair work difficult and expensive as a considerable amount
of planking must be removed to replace even a small area of
decay in the inner skin or stringers. The treatment of all the
faying surfaces with preservative will reduce risk of decay in
double-skinned boats.

Inadequate provision for the ventilation in the bilge spaces
and behind linings is a common cause of dampness and rot
in boats.

Prevention of Decay in Boats

Rot in vessels, as in buildings, may develop as a result either of faulty construction and the use of inferior or unsuitable materials, or through neglecting to maintain the vessel in a good state of repair. If the original construction is faulty greater care in maintenance will, of course, be necessary if trouble is to be avoided.

Constructional Precautions

Sound, well-seasoned timber of the appropriate kind should be used in the construction of the vessel. Since Teak is no longer generally available for the building of private boats, and supplies of good quality Rock Elm are very scarce, it is often necessary to select some other wood. For the framing timbers English Oak and Wych Elm can be used instead of imported Elm. Provided that sapwood is rigorously excluded, home-grown Oak is, of course, much more durable than Elm. Among the less familiar woods now being imported into the United Kingdom there are a number which are suitable for boat building. For keels, stems, stern and rudder posts, etc., the following woods, all of which are durable, should be suitable: Kokrodua (*Afrormosia*); Afzelia; Iroko; Makoré; Opepe, and Dahoma. For bent frames, gunwales, etc., a good alternative to imported Elm is Danta, which is more resistant to decay than Elm, and bends well. As an alternative to African Mahogany for planking, Agba, which is more durable, should prove useful.

Careful attention should be paid to constructional details that will prevent the entry of fresh water, *particularly through deck seams*. The use of a waterproof roofing material between the deck beams and the planking, which is sometimes used in barges, might be considered. What is really needed is a satisfactory seamless deck covering. Moisture is especially liable to enter through exposed end grain, or when the grain has been damaged. Treatment of end-surfaces with thick lead paint before joints are put together and on all faying surfaces is helpful.

Plumbing fixtures should be examined at intervals, and the slightest leak of fresh water dealt with immediately. Much of the rot that has occurred in Fairmile M.T.B.s was attributed to leakage from plumbing. Where possible, fresh-water pumps and sinks should be sited in the centre line so that any leakage goes straight to the bottom of the bilges.

However good the design and the workmanship may be, a certain amount of moisture must inevitably find its way into a boat and this can be removed only by adequate ventilation to *all* parts of the vessel. When a boat is at sea only for short periods, and spends most of her time at anchor, some mechanical means for circulating the air through the "dead" air spaces may be necessary, and it is the usual practice in lifeboats to run a fan at regular intervals which drives air through the water-tight compartments.

Unnecessary linings should be dispensed with, and provision made for ventilating the space between any linings and the external skin. Deck head linings are particularly dangerous as they may hide any deck leakage and prevent detection of incipient decay. Leakage at covering board seams on to the beam shelves and frame heads may go undiscovered behind linings for years and cause severe damage. Detailed suggestions for ventilating dead air spaces are given in Duff's third paper.

Use of Preservatives

A preservative should be applied freely to the woodwork at known danger points, particularly if any of the less durable kinds of timber or plywood are employed. Tar-oil products are not generally used in boats as they interfere with subsequent painting operations, but there would be no objection to using them on timbers in the bilges where painting can with advantage be omitted provided the preservative treatment has been very thorough. Solvent type preservatives, particularly those based on copper naphthenate, have, in recent years, been used extensively by boat builders. When deciding what preservative to use on boat timbers consideration should be given to the possibility of interaction between the chemicals in the preservative and metalwork in the carft.

Treatment of boat timbers is usually carried out by brushing or dipping, and so far very little pressure-treated timber has been used for this purpose, the reason being that the members are often of large size and made from woods that are resistant to impregnation. Also a good deal of cutting and framing has to be done in the yard and, if this has to be carried out on impregnated timbers, untreated wood below the depth of the impregnation might become exposed. There are, however, certain types of craft, such as barges, scows and catamarans, that might well be constructed of pressure-creosoted timber. Probably certain structural members, such as the stringers, which are often made of non-durable timber, could with advantage receive pressure treatment with a water soluble preservative.

Choice of Plywood

Plywood is generally made with veneers of a relatively non-durable timber such as Birch or Beech, and even if the glue is a synthetic resin which in itself is resistant to moisture and immune to decomposition by micro-organisms, the plywood as a whole can readily be attacked by wood-rotting fungi. During the war large numbers of M.T.B.s built by the Fairmile technique were constructed with plywood frames in which decay subsequently proved very troublesome. Fungal infection enters through the edges of the plywood, often decaying the internal laminations without affecting the surface veneers.

Unless special plywood made of a naturally durable timber is available it should always receive thorough treatment with a preservative if there is any possibility of its becoming damp in service. If Mahogany plywood is used the purchaser should make sure that *all* the veneers are in fact made of Mahogany, and that the core is not made of a less-durable wood such as Obeche. Plywood for boat building should conform to British Standard Specification No. 1088, *Plywood for Marine Craft.*

Maintenance

No unnecessary restriction of ventilation should be permitted, and any adjustable ventilators should be fully opened in fair weather.

A periodic inspection of the bilges and of all other enclosed spaces should be made. Any shavings or pieces of wood that fall into the bilges should be removed.

Corticene and other floor coverings should be kept in good repair, especially in bathrooms and lavatories.

Any leakage of water should be reported and checked with the minimum of delay and the defects responsible for it should be sought for and remedied.

Treatment of Decay

When decay is found in any part of a vessel a careful survey should be made at once to determine its full extent. All the woodwork in the vicinity of the decayed piece should be tested by prodding it hard with a pointed tool. In the case of plywood, however, a blow from a light hammer may reveal internal decay which might be missed by simple probing as the point may fail to penetrate the sound veneers on the surface. Sometimes fungal growths are visible on the surface of the decayed wood, but there may also quite often be decay hidden beneath an undamaged painted surface. Warping, collapse, cracking and

243

discoloration of the surface should immediately arouse suspicions and areas showing any of these symptoms should be tested with especial care.

The next step is to cut away all the decayed wood, with at least a few inches margin of apparently sound wood, and this should be removed from the ship and burnt. The cut ends of the sound timbers thus exposed should be thoroughly treated, at least twice, with solvent type or aqueous wood preservative. All new timber used in repairs should be given several full brush coats of preservative. Only well-seasoned wood should be used for repairs.

Rot in Refrigerated Ships

Extensive outbreaks of decay have occurred in the wood linings of the refrigerated holds in meat-and fruit-carrying ships, due to condensation of moisture in the linings setting up conditions favourable for development of wood-rotting fungi. Decay is most likely to occur in vessels carrying fruit, such as bananas, which are kept at temperatures above freezing point, at which fungal decay can take place. Most of the decay in the cases examined by the author was caused either by *Coniophora cerebella* or by species of *Poria*.

Serious decay in the cool stores used for food storage in passenger liners and in warships has also been reported. Though no decay can occur in woodwork that is kept permanently below freezing point the outer part of the framework behind the linings of cold stores is often well above it and therefore vulnerable. Rot can also become established during periods when the cold rooms are not refrigerated while the timber is still saturated with condensed moisture. The only certain method of protecting this woodwork is to impregnate it with a water soluble preservative which will not taint foodstuffs. A copper chrome preservative has been extensively and successfully used for this purpose. Thorough brush treatment of the framing and lining with an effective water soluble preservative will also afford fairly good protection.

CHEMICAL BREAKDOWN OF WOOD IN BOATS

Occasionally, wood around fastenings becomes darkened and discoloured, and a depression around the nail appears. Finally, a split an inch or two long may develop on each side of the fastenings. This so-called "nail sickness" may lead to the fastenings becoming loose and even to leakage of water. It has been shown that this type of damage results from the action of chemicals released from sea water by galvanic action. If two dissimilar metals are embedded in wet wood (which always contains electrolytes in solution) they can form the poles of a galvanic cell. Corrosion takes place in the metal forming the anode and hydroxyl ions are discharged at the cathode. The wood around the anode thus becomes acidic while alkaline conditions develop around the cathode. Breakdown of wood substance can occur as a result of either condition. Copper nails themselves may become extensively corroded.

Trouble seems most liable to occur in double-skinned boats, and sea water is much more active than fresh on account of its salt content. Slight electrical leakage will greatly accelerate the action, and stray electric currents of very low amperage can cause serious trouble. Possibly the reason why this type of damage has become more prevalent in recent years is because so many more vessels now carry electrical gear such as radio, and electric sounding apparatus for fishing, which is not always properly earthed.

Prevention of chemical breakdown of the wood depends on avoiding, as far as possible, the introduction of dissimilar metals into wet wood, and the careful avoidance of any electrical

245

S

leakages. Coating certain types of fastenings with bituminous paint may be a palliative measure.

Marine Borers

Fungal decay plays a minor part in bringing about the destruction of timber in the sea. Though many fungi have been found in timber and cordage saturated with sea water, their action is generally confined to the surface layers of the wood and is therefore relatively slow, but it does predispose the wood to attack by Gribble (see below). Few wood-boring insects live in the sea, but timber in salt and brackish water is frequently subject to the attack of Marine Borers, especially in the warmer parts of the world. Marine Borers are, as has already been explained, of two types, namely bivalve molluscs and crustaceans.

Shipworms

The most destructive of the Marine Borers are the bivalve molluscs known as Shipworms—the *Calamitus navium* of Linnaeus—which have been recognized since classical times as a menace to wooden ships. They can also cause extensive damage to shore-based structures and marine works. In 1730-33 damage by Shipworms to the wooden dykes protecting large areas in Holland was so severe as to threaten wide-scale flooding. During the First World War one species caused damage to the harbour works in San Francisco Bay which was estimated at ten million dollars.

There are many different kinds of Shipworm in different parts of the ocean but only two, *Teredo navalis* and *Teredo norvegica*, are of real economic importance in British waters. *T. navalis* is the more widely distributed having been carried all over the world by wooden ships. *T. norvegica* has a relatively more northern distribution and appears to be able to breed

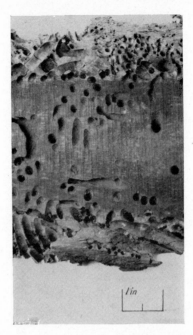

Fig. 55. Shipworm damage. A.
Damage by *Teredo* in sapwood
of Pyinkado. Scale shown.

over most of the year whereas *T. navalis* breeds actively only
at temperatures over 15°C. Each female is capable of producing
several million larvæ. They start life as tiny free-swimming
larvæ which appear to be attracted to wood on which they soon
settle down and begin to bore. The larvæ then change into
adult form, the shell altering to become an efficient cutting
tool instead of a protective covering. The body becomes
long and wormlike and the shell covers only its front tip. Two
syphons that circulate sea water around the animal project
a short way from a small hole in the wood, and when these
are withdrawn the animal can close the opening into the burrow,

247

thus retaining the water in the burrow and enabling it to survive quite long periods of exposure to the air.

As the animal grows so the diameter of the burrow enlarges and may reach as much as a quarter of an inch. At first the burrows tend to follow the grain of the wood but later they twist and turn so that finally the wood may be completely riddled though its external surface remains more or less intact. (See Fig. 55.) The burrows, which never actually cross (unlike those of the piddocks in rock), can reach a length of as much

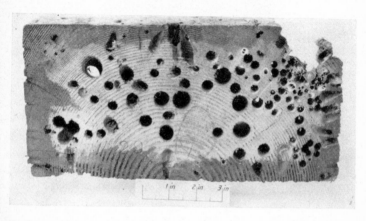

B. Severe damage by *Teredo* sp. in Douglas Fir which had been insufficiently creosoted. Specimen taken from marine structure in sea off Malaya. Note pear shaped borings of *Martesia* near edges. Scale in inches shown.

as four feet. *Teredo* are able to digest cellulose in the wood so that they can derive energy from the wood into which they are boring. They occur around the coasts of Great Britain south of the Clyde and the Forth, but cause serious damage only around the southern half of England. The damage they cause is somewhat sporadic and its intensity seems to depend largely on the temperature of the water. Though *Teredo* demands some salt in the water it can live in brackish water provided that it contains over 5-9 parts of salt per 1000 (average salinity of sea water is 35 per 1000). There is little risk of *Teredo* attack if the water is heavily polluted with silt, sewage or factory effluents.

Martesia, another molluscan borer, has its body encased in the bivalve shell. It is essentially a pest of tropical waters, and does not cause damage in colder seas. It forms pear-shaped cavities (See Fig. 55.) which rarely exceed $2\frac{1}{2}$ in. in length and 1 in. in diameter.

Gribble

The crustacean wood borers are very common all around the coasts of Great Britain. The true Gribble, *Limnoria lignorum*, which is about 1/6 in. long and looks something like a small edition of the common woodlouse, makes superficial burrows so that the damage it causes is always obvious. Its attack is always most active about low-water level. As the surface of the wood is broken up by the action of these animals (which may be present in enormous numbers, i.e. several hundred to the square inch) it is removed by the scouring action of the waves, thus exposing fresh surfaces to infestation. The diameter of piles can thus become progressively reduced until they finally fail completely. (See Fig. 56.)

There is no evidence that Gribble can digest wood substance and it probably feeds mainly on the micro-organisms growing on, and in, the wood. The presence of superficial soft rot caused by cellulose-destroying marine fungi undoubtedly renders wood more susceptible to attack by these animals and some authorities maintain that Gribbles are unable to attack wood at all if it is perfectly sound.

Another crustacean wood borer is *Chelura terebrans* which is somewhat larger than *Limnoria*. It is usually found in

249

association with the latter, living in the more superficial layers of the wood that have already been honeycombed by *Limnoria*.

The presence of Marine Borers in timber specimens and the extent of their borings can be readily established by X-ray photography, but care must be taken not to let the wood dry out unevenly before it is photographed. The advantage of this non-destructive method of examination is that the progress of attack in individual samples can be followed over a period of time.

Fig. 56. Jetty pile almost eaten through at base by the Gribble, *Limnoria lignorum*.

Protection of Timber against Marine Borers.

Though no timber is completely immune to the attack of Marine Borers some kinds are highly resistant, especially in temperate regions, and can be used for marine structure without preservative treatment. (See Table 6.). Other timbers can be protected from attack either by sheathing them with a material which prevents the borers from reaching the wood, or by impregnating with a substance poisonous to borers. Copper has proved to be the best material for sheathing boats, though Muntz metal sometimes gives good results. Concrete is more suitable for encasing piling and several methods for applying this have been used commercially. Impregnation with coal-tar creosote has been shown, as the results of trials in many parts of the world, to give the most consistently effective protection against *Teredo*. Though *Limnoria* can sometimes attack creosoted wood it usually does little damage to it. Impregnation of wood with a copper chrome preservative has also given very good protection in some waters.

Attack of Gribble on boat timbers can largely be prevented by maintaining unbroken the paint film on the surface of the timber which is in contact with the sea water. Thorough soaking with a solution of copper naphthenate also gives fairly good protection to boat timbers.

Professor C. M. Yonge states that an effective method of destroying Shipworms after they have penetrated timber is to detonate an explosive charge in the water close to the infected piles so that the blast wave will kill the animals in the wood. After the wood had been freed in this way from infection it should be possible to provide an inert coating to prevent reinfestation.

TABLE 6.—*Timbers resistant to Marine Borers.*

Latin Name	Trade Name
Afrormosia elata	Afrormosia
Cyclodiscus gabunensis	Okan
Dicorynia paraensis	Basralocus
Eschweilera sp.	Manbarklak
Eucalyptus marginata	Jarrah
Eusideroxylon zwageri	Billian or Belian
Lophira alata	Ekki
Ocotea rodiaei	Greenheart
Ocotea rubra	Red Louro
Pterocarpus soyauxii	African Padauk
Sarcocephalus diderichii	Opepe
Syncarpia laurifolia	Australian Turpentine
Tristania conferta	Brush Box
Xylia dolabriformis	Pyinkado

Decay in Vehicles, Aircraft, Poles, Mining Timbers, Cooling Towers, Packing-cases, Fibreboards, Plywood, etc.

VEHICLES

THE early motor-cars contained a considerable amount of woodwork, the frame of the body and hood usually being constructed of ash or some similar timber. In temperate climates the amount of decay that occurred during the normal life of a car was seldom sufficiently great to excite much comment, or to be the subject of serious complaints. In the wet tropics, however, the situation was very different, and in the 'twenties it was by no means uncommon for the bodywork of cars to become so severely decayed that they had to be entirely reconstructed after a few years' service. Humphrey, who studied this problem in the Philippines, reported how in that country it was often necessary to rebuild the body of imported cars with durable native woods after only two years in the islands.

When the export market became so important to British manufacturers the question of protecting the woodwork began to be taken seriously, and many makers applied a preservative to all the wooden parts that go into a car. The method employed was to dip or spray the parts, after they had been fashioned to their final shape, in a solvent type preservative. Copper naphthenate solutions were extensively used, but some makers had special preservatives prepared which, in addition to preserving the wood, stained it black. Today much less wood is used in the bodywork, but a certain amount is generally required for fixing the upholstery and it is desirable that this should receive preservative treatment. It was not unusual to find in old cars extensive decay in the wooden parts below sliding roofs and runningboards, and fruit bodies of various fungi such as *Polystictus versicolor* and *Lenzites trabea* have been found growing from such woodwork. When repairing these old cars it is important to treat any new timber to be used in them thoroughly with a preservative, as it may be difficult to prevent the entry of moisture.

Extensive decay has been found in the bodies of motor-buses, probably due to the fact that they are frequently washed with powerful hoses that force water into any open or loose joints. Heavy condensation on the windows in winter is another source of dampness which may reach the woodwork. While improved detailing may reduce the risk of moisture penetration at the vital points there will still always be a chance of some water getting into the bodywork when the vehicle has been on the road for some time and the joints have begun to open up a little as the result of the frequent flexing of the structural members occasioned by constant stopping and starting. The cost of repairs to bodywork is always high and it is definitely a worthwhile precaution to treat the timber with preservative while the body is being built.

Comparatively little trouble with rot and decay in the bodywork of trucks and lorries has been reported in this country, but in military and commercial vehicles designed for service overseas all woodwork should receive preservative treatment before it is painted. Several instances of rot in ambulancos in use in the tropics have been reported, and unless the wood used in the construction of these vehicles is a naturally durable kind it should likewise be treated.

Caravans, which often have to stand out in the open throughout the year, are very liable to decay if any leakage of water occurs and all the vulnerable parts of their woodwork should therefore receive preservative treatment. Any plywood used in the construction of the body of the van should be "external grade" and bonded with a synthetic resin adhesive.

Farm carts, especially those used for carrying dung, should be treated with preservatives at intervals if they are not painted. Regular treatment of the floor boards with creosote will prolong their life.

Aircraft

Although most modern aircraft are of all-metal construction a certain number of training 'planes, light aircraft and gliders are still being made of wood. In the past decay occurred in this country only in aircraft parked in the open and exposed to the weather for prolonged periods, but in tropical countries it was found more frequently. The introduction of modern synthetic resin glues for bonding the plywood and for assembly work has greatly reduced the risk of general deterioration as a result of exposure to damp conditions.

Timber for the construction of aircraft must be carefully selected to avoid the inclusion of any traces of dote which would seriously reduce the strength of the wood, and also involve the risk of subsequent spread of decay should any moisture reach it.

Drain holes should always be located at the lowest point in any aircraft component into which there is any risk of water penetrating, so as to avoid the risk of water remaining in them for any length of time.

Vulnerable parts of wooden aircraft intended for use in damp, tropical climates can with advantage be treated with a solvent type preservative. As some glues do not adhere well to treated wood it is safer to apply the preservative after assembly of the components.

Poles In Service

If poles are not adequately seasoned before they are impregnated with creosote, or other wood preservative, it is unlikely that the sapwood will be fully treated throughout its thickness. There is therefore a risk that when the pole eventually dries out completely in hot, dry weather it will split and the untreated sapwood will then be exposed to airborne infection by spores that fall into these cracks and splits, or are washed down into them. In this way the dangerous condition known as "shell rot" becomes established without there being any visible indication on the surface of the pole, which remains hard and undamaged. The strength of the pole may thus become seriously reduced and dangerous for the linesmen who climb it with spiked climbing irons on their feet. As the immediate surface of the pole is generally hard and firm the hidden shell rot will not be discovered by prodding with a pointed tool. Striking the pole with a hammer which gives a ringing note is the better method and will often reveal the presence of rot to the ear of an experienced inspector, particularly if actual cavities have developed. The use of X-rays to reveal internal flaws is, of course, common practice in metal structures and attempts have been made to use X-rays to detect internal decay in piling and transmission poles. The differential absorption of gamma radiation from a cobalt-60 source by sound and decayed wood has been suggested by Japanese workers in this field as a method for detecting heart rot in standing trees, and this might also prove useful for detecting internal decay in piling and other large structural timbers.

Internal decay below the treated zone also occurs in large sized baulks if there are deep seated pockets of incipient decay which escape treatment. I have seen this condition develop into extensive and serious decay in large baulks of Douglas Fir forming part of a jetty. Since it is almost impossible to obtain penetration exceeding about one inch in depth in this timber the only safeguard is to sterilize the baulk throughout its thickness by steaming it, or by keeping it in hot creosote at 150°F until this temperature is attained right through the wood. The time required to heat an 18 in. green pile throughout to this temperature will be about 15 hr, and even longer for a seasoned pile. Though this is an additional expense, experience has shown that it is a worth-while precaution when using Douglas Fir in very large sizes for external structures.

Mining Timbers

The conditions in many mines are extraordinarily favourable for the growth of fungi, so that once decay has become established in them it will spread with alarming rapidity. The atmospheric humidity is often very high, particularly in the return airways where the circulating air is charged with moisture which it has picked up on its journey through the workings. In shallow pits liquid water may find its way into the galleries and saturate the timber. The temperature remains suitable for fungal growth throughout the year and in the deeper mines may be as high as 75-80°F, which, if any moisture is present, is ideal for the rapid growth of all kinds of fungi. In this country, however, the deeper mines are usually fairly dry and the risk of decay is less than it is in the shallow ones, but in the South African gold mines there is a serious risk of timber decay even at the deeper levels. Many different kinds of fungi can be found on pitwood, but the exact species are often difficult to recognize as the fructifications that they form in the dark are sometimes quite abnormal. *Lentinus lepideus*, for instance, forms stag's horn-like growths in place of typical toadstools. Probably the commonest fungus in our coal mines in *Poria vaillantii*, which often forms magnificent white tassels several feet long, that hang from the cross props like stalactites. (See Fig. 57.) *Coniophora* is also common and does a great deal of damage.

257

While the prpos at the coal face are in use for only a short time (possibly only a few days), the large quantities of timber that are employed elsewhere, for the support of the roof along roadways and airways, and for shaft linings and sleepers, may be needed for many years. Even though in most coal mines

Fig. 57. Vigorous growth of *Poria vaillantii* hanging from decayed pit props in a damp coal mine.

steel arches are now used for supporting the roof, timber may be required above them for lagging, and wooden props are still used for supporting the permanent roadways in some of the smaller collieries, and in various underground workings other than coal mines. That all mine timbers should be assured of the maximum resistance to decay is obviously of the utmost importance, both from the point of view of safety and economy.

Though it is sometimes possible by increasing the ventilation in a mine to reduce the atmospheric humidity, and therbey to retard decay of the pitwood, it is only by preservative treatment that immunity from decay can be assured.

Experiments carried out at two collieries by the Forest Products Research Laboratory have shown that impregnation of props with cheap water soluble preservatives, by the hot and cold open-tank process, can very greatly extend their life, even under conditions highly conducive to rapid decay. In these two mines, where the average life of untreated props was only about two years, props that had been impregnated with a 2 per cent solution of sodium fluoride, zinc chloride, or "Wolman salts" were almost all sound after 17 years underground.

The most suitable preservatives for pitwood are the water soluble ones for they are cheap, clean and odourless, and they tend to diminish rather than to increase the inflammability of the timber. A 2 per cent solution of sodium fluoride or of sodium borate will give adequate protection provided that there has been reasonably good absorption. An average retention of $1/4$ to $1/2$ lb of dry salt per cubic foot of timber can be considered adequate. Since the treated timber is not exposed to the leaching action of rain there is little risk of the preservative being washed out of the timber, even if the salts do not become "fixed" in the wood.

In the gold mines on the Rand in South Africa very large quantities of timber are used annually; for instance, it was estimated that approximately £ 3,000,000 were spent in 1940 on timber for mining purposes, so that any increase in the life of the timber obtained by the use of preservatives may effect noteworthy economies. Timber treated with the patented "yard mixture", which consisted of 3.0 per cent zinc sulphate plus 0.3 per cent "Wolman triolith", showed only slight signs of decay after seven years underground, in situations where untreated timber had rotted completely within eighteen months.

There is, then, ample evidence to prove that preservation of pitwood, in mines where conditions are favourable for fungal growth, is a paying proposition. The extra cost involved in impregnating pit props should not, with efficient organization, exceed one-third of the cost of the timber itself, and this cost may be recovered many times over by the saving on new props and the cost of the labour for installing them.

A preservative containing fire-retardant salts can be used if it is considered desirable to render the pitwood fire resistant. Since decayed wood is, in any case, much more readily ignited than sound wood, preservation against decay does, in itself, decrease the risk from fire.

Underground shoring and trench linings should always receive preservative treatment, as, though they may remain for only a short time in any one situation, repeated contact with damp earth may easily set up decay. Also it must be remembered that many structures designed for only temporary use are often required to last much longer than was originally intended. Trench air-raid shelters, constructed in 1939 and lined with untreated timber (much of it good quality Douglas Fir) had mostly become dangerous by 1943 owing to decay of the timbering, and needed to be replaced.

Decay of such timbering often escapes detection for a considerable time, as the visible surfaces, which are exposed to the air, may remain sound although decay has attacked the face that is in contact with the soil. Regular and careful inspection of timber of this kind is necessary in order to detect decay at an early stage. Any timber that has to remain in contact with the ground for any length of time should be impregnated under pressure with a preservative. If pressure treated timber cannot be obtained the wood should be given a dip treatment, or brushed over twice with creosote which will help to delay the onset of decay; but it must again be emphasized that such superficial treatment can at best give only temporary protection to timber that is to come into contact with the earth.

Cooling Towers

Very large quantities of timber are used in the construction of towers for cooling the condenser water at power stations. Some of the older of these towers were constructed entirely of timber; but the modern towers usually consist of a concrete shell in which there is a framework carrying the tiers of timber slats, or "louvres", over which the hot water flows. These louvres, which are usually wedge shaped and a few inches wide, may last for twenty years or so, but occasionally fail very much sooner, necessitating retimbering at great expense. Formerly it was considered that most of the breakdown of the wood was due to prolonged exposure to hot water, but it has now been found that most of the deterioration is the result of fungal decay caused by the cellulose destroying micro-fungi which cause soft rot.

Examining a cross-section of an old louvre from a tower one usually finds a thin layer on the surface that is completely decayed and which cracks up and flakes away on drying, but beneath this layer the core of the louvre appears to be completely sound. Microscopic examination of the layer of cells immediately next to the decomposed surface reveals the presence of large numbers of fungal hyphæ which are tunnelling longitudinally in the thickness of the cell walls. If a cross section of the wood in this area be examined under the microscope a series of holes will be observed in the secondary cell walls of the tracheids. The fungi concerned in this type of breakdwon are not wood-rotting *Basidiomycetes* but rather are they the

261

T

cellulose-destroying *Ascomycetes* such as species of *Chaetomium* and *Fungi imperfecti*.

Effective protection of the filling timber in cooling towers can be given by impregnating them with copper/chrome/arsenic preservatives which become highly fixed in the wood. Retention of about 1.25 lb of dry salt per cubic foot of timber, using solution strengths of 5.0 per cent or over, are generally called for. Timber impregnated in this way according to the specifications laid down by the Central Electricity Generating Board is expected to last at least 30 years—except when the circulating water is contaminated with sea water in which case rather more rapid deterioration may be expected.

Packing-cases

In this country it is unusual for packing-cases to be exposed to damp conditions long enough to become decayed. But during the war, when stores had to be held in supply depots where no proper storage facilities were available, and where cases were often left on the ground for weeks or even months, serious deterioration occurred, especially in the Far Eastern theatres of war. Special methods for preserving the stores themselves were soon developed and both the equipment and the packing materials were "tropicalized". Specially treated cardboards, that retained their strength even after they had been wetted, were manufactured and used for the cartons and containers. The wooden packing-cases themselves were made from timber that had been treated with a preservative. Solutions of copper naphthenate were used extensively for this purpose. If it is wished to protect packing-cases required for foodstuffs a non-poisonous water-soluble preservative, such as borax, or a mixture of borax and boric acid in equal parts, should be used.

Cases that have to be stored for indefinite periods underground should, if possible, be made of impregnated timber, and it is now common practice to impregnate ammunition boxes with a water soluble preservative.

It is often necessary to stencil labels or instructions on the outside of a packing-case, and when this is so a preservative must be chosen that will not render the wood too dark in colour, or incapable of retaining the paint used on the stencils.

Crates to be used for the transport of bottles can with advantage receive treatment with an aqueous or a solvent type preservative, as they are often kept in damp cellars or stored in the open when not in use and so, if not treated, are liable to decay in the course of time.

If cases are made of unseasoned timber that contains much sapwood they may become mouldy. While the presence of mould does not weaken the case it does spoil its appearance, and also may obscure any distinctive lettering. Manufacturers of soap and firms packing foodstuffs very much dislike having to send out their goods in stained or mouldy cases. Some moulds produce a strong musty odour and this may be picked up by the foodstuffs. If metal goods are packed in cases made from unseasoned timber severe corrosion may result, which is yet another reason for having boxboards thoroughly dry before they are made into cases. If supplies of air-seasoned timber are not available the boards should be kiln dried. But even if the wood is properly seasoned evaporation from certain goods, such as soap, which themselves contain a good deal of moisture, may render it damp enough to allow mould to grow.

If, for these special purposes, treatment of the wood with an antiseptic is considered advisable, care must be taken to select one that will not taint the product to be cyarried. Solutions of "Shirlan" or borax can be used with safety, and so, for many purposes, can sodium pentachlorophenate. There is little or no risk of any wrapped goods being affected by any one of these antiseptics, but expert advice should be sought before treatment is applied to boards that may come into direct contact with foodstuffs. Mould is sometimes troublesome on chip baskets, or punnets, that may have to be stored for many months in unheated damp buildings, and a method has recently been described in the U.S.A. for protecting such berry baskets by dipping them for 15 sec in molten wax (95 per cent paraffin wax M.P. 143-150°F and 5 per cent micro-crystalline wax M.P. 160-165°F).

Plywood

Before the discovery of synthetic resin adhesives plywood could not be employed successfully where there was any risk of its becoming damp. Ordinary animal glue, made from hides, is readily soluble in water, and plywood bonded with this quickly deteriorates on being wetted. Casein adhesives retain some of their strength even in a moist condition and the bond recovers its strength when the plywood is again dried; but these adhesives can soon be decomposed by the action of micro-organisms if damp conditions persist. Other adhesives of a protein nature such as blood albumin and soya bean protein are likewise soon decomposed under damp conditions, and although their resistance to breakdown can be greatly enhanced by the addition of antiseptics such as pentachlorophenol, none of them can be relied on indefinitely to resist microbial attack if the dampness persists.

The development of synthetic resin adhesives, which are resistant both to direct solution by water and to the attacks of moulds and bacteria under moist conditions, has greatly extended the uses to which plywood can be put. These adhesives have been based mainly upon urea formaldehyde and phenol formaldehyde synthetic resins, and more recently resorcinol compounds have been developed.

Plywood bonded with these synthetic resin glues does not delaminate even if it is exposed to moisture for long periods.

This type of plywood, which is generally sold as "exterior grade", is now available commercially at a reasonable price; but it must be remembered that, even if the glues are resistant to breakdown, the plywood made with them is not, unless it has received preservative treatment, significantly more resistant to decay than is the wood from which its constituent veneers were cut. Considerable quantities of birch and gaboon plywood bonded with U.F. resin were used for the frames in motor torpedo-boats constructed during the last war. Some of this plywood has since suffered extensive decay where it has been exposed to persistently damp conditions. Pontoons made with a plywood skin similarly deteriorated when left exposed to the weather over long periods.

Plywood can be treated after manufacture with ordinary wood preservatives applied by brushing, or by impregnation. Only if the plywood is bonded with a glue which is a moisture-resistant synthetic resin can it safely be impregnated with an aqueous preservative. Surface application of preservative will probably give adequate protection to plywood unless it is brought into prolonged contact with the ground, as plywood is much less likely than is solid wood to develop deep cracks and checks that will expose untreated wood below the treated surface. Most plywood used for external work receives a coat of paint for decorative purposes and to prevent weathering of the exposed surface, and this film of paint will help to retain in the wood any preservative applied to the surface. Since wood-rotting fungi often gain access to the core of plywood through the edges of the sheets where end grain is exposed, particular attention should be paid to thorough treatment of all cut edges.

Plywood can be effectively protected during manufacture against insect attack and fungal decay by immersing the freshly cut veneers in a concentrated solution of a water-borne preservative, and then block stacking the sheets for a few hours to

265

permit diffusion of the preservative. Sodium pentaborate applied in this way was found, in Australia, to be outstandingly effective for this purpose.

Plywood bonded with animal glue is very susceptible to the attack of the Common Furniture Beetle, and for this reason such plywood should receive preservative treatment when it is to be used in a building. When an attic space is being converted into a bedroom or workroom plywood is often fixed to the existing rafter, and these may already be infested with woodworm which will soon spread to the plywood. Meter-boards, made of thick plywood, are generally fixed in some out-of-the-way spot which may well be damp, and it is very common to find them pulverized with Furniture Beetle. Thorough treatment with several applications of tar oil or solvent type preservative will greatly reduce the risk of infestation.

It is possible by incorporating in the glue a powerful insecticide, such as benzene hexachloride (at the rate of $1/4$ lb in the glue required to spread over 1000 ft^2 of glue line), to render plywood resistant to infestation for at least a period of several years; but plywood treated in this way is not generally available commercially in this country.

Oak-faced plywood that has been fixed to a damp wall sometimes develops large, unsightly, dark brown stains, caused (as was explained in Chapter 5) by the decomposition of the animal glue releasing sufficient ammonia to "fume" the wood. If plywood is to be fixed to a wall where there is any likelihood of damp the back of the plywood should be thoroughly painted with an aluminium primer or a bituminous paint to reduce the absorption of moisture, and means should be devised for ventilating the space between the plywood and the wall.

Specially resistant types of plywood in which the veneers of wood are themselves impregnated with synthetic resin before being bonded together with a resin glue are being developed and promise to be a really durable sheet material.

Some of the so-called "improved woods" which contain quite a high proportion of synthetic resin and highly compressed thin veneers of wood are extremely resistant to fungal attack.

Wall Boards

Wall boards are of two types—soft insulating boards and compressed hardboards comparable in their properties to plywood. Both types can be manufactured from wood pulp and waste cellulose material such as sugar-cane bagasse, and may contain, in consequence, much material that can be decomposed by wood-destroying fungi, or consumed by termites. On the whole the hardboards, which sometimes contain waterproofing materials, are more resistant to fungal decay than the insulating boards, most of which decompose readily if exposed to prolonged periods of dampness. Insulating boards are sometimes fixed to the underside of a cold roof and during wintry weather may become saturated with condensed moisture and thereby become mouldy and decayed. Boards containing preservatives such as salts of arsenic have been prepared for use in tropical countries and are said to be resistant to termite attack, and efforts are now being made to manufacture a board that will be immune to fungal decay. Complete immunity to attack under severe conditions of exposure has not yet been achieved, but some of the boards in which an antiseptic has been incorporated show greatly increased resistance compared with ordinary untreated boards. It is, of course, always possible to apply a preservative to the board after its manufacture, and this should be done if there is known to be a risk of dampness in the situation where the board is to be used.

Wood wool and cement blocks are fairly resistant to fungal decay, but they may become permeated with the strands of *Merulius lacrymans* in a building where there is an active outbreak of dry rot. After prolonged exposure to Dry Rot Fungus softening of the blocks occurs, the fibres become brittle and the cement binding them together becomes weakened, presumably by the action of the acids produced by the fungus. Wood wool blocks should not be used in any situation where they are likely to remain permanently damp.

Cork and Cork Products

Cork itself (and particularly baked cork) is one of the most resistant of all plant products to decomposition. Though slight mould growths can develop on granulated cork under very moist conditions this does not cause any breakdown in the cork itself. Cork slab is therefore an excellent material for insulating cold stores and constant temperature chambers.

CONCLUSION

The steadily increasing demands for forest products throughout the world, which is reflected in the greatly increased prices for timber and for wood pulp that have been ruling since the end of World War II emphasize the vital necessity for conserving existing supplies and preventing any unnecessary wastage. These considerations should weigh particularly heavily here in Great Britain where such a high proportion of our needs for timber and wood pulp have to be met by imports, and there is no doubt that as the causes of decay and the value of preservative treatment become more widely understood and appreciated, so will more and more timber receive adequate protection and proper care during its preparation, storage and use.

Further research is needed to elucidate some of the outstanding problems involved in the production and shipment of clean timber, and in the prevention of deterioration in its storage and use, particularly as regards some of the hitherto unknown tropical woods now being imported. Within the limits of this book it has only been possible to describe the more prevalent types of decay and the conditions under which they are likely to occur, and to give some general advice as to how to prevent and cure them. For more detailed information on these and kindred subjects those interested are referred to the publications listed in the bibliography.

Bibliography

Cartwright, K. St. G., and Findlay, W. P. K., *Decay of Timber and its Prevention*, 2nd edition. H.M.S.O. London (1958).

Findlay, W. P. K., *The Preservation of Timber*. London (1961).

Van Groenou, H. B., Rischen, H. W. L., and van den Berg, J., *Wood Preservation during the Last Fifty Years*. Leiden (1951).

Harris, W. V., *Termites, their Recognition and Control*. London (1961).

Hickin, N.E., *The Insect Factor in Wood Decay*. London (1963).

Hunt, G.M., and Garratt, G. A., *Wood Preservation*, 2nd edition. New York and London (1958).

Le Sueur, A. D. C., *The Care and Repair of Ornamental Trees*. London (1934).

Mahlke-Troschel and Liese, J., *Handbuch der Holzkonservierung*, 3rd edition. Berlin (1950).

Morris Thomas, A., and White, M. G., *The Sterilization of Insect Infected Wood by High Frequency Heating*. Electrical Research Association Technical Report. W/T37. (1959).

Martinez, J. Benito, *Conservacion de Maderas en Sus Aspectus Teorico Industrial y Economico*. Madrid (1952).

Peace, T. R., *Diseases of Trees and Shrubs*. Oxford (1962).

Smith, D. N., *The Natural Durability of Timber*. 2nd edition. Forest Products Research Record. No 30. H.M.S.O. London (1959).

Much information of interest to the student of timber pests and diseases is contained in the records of the annual conventions of the British Wood Preserving Association obtainable from its office in 6, Southampton Place, London, W.C.1, and in the proceedings of the American Wood Preservers Association published annually in the U.S.A.

Index/Glossary